FLY-BY-NIGHT

K. M. Peyton

FLY - BY - NIGHT

ILLUSTRATED BY
THE AUTHOR

London
OXFORD UNIVERSITY PRESS
1971

Oxford University Press, Ely House, London W.1

GLASGOW NEW YORK TORONTO MELBOURNE WELLINGTON
CAPE TOWN SALISBURY IBADAN NAIROBI DAR ES SALAAM LUSAKA ADDIS ABABA
BOMBAY CALCUTTA MADRAS KARACHI LAHORE DACCA
KUALA LUMPUR SINGAPORE HONG KONG TOKYO

TO
Hilary and Cracker

Printed in Holland
Zuid-Nederlandsche Drukkerij N.V.
's-Hertogenbosch

CONTENTS

1 Ruth's Day Out

The little green book was very dog-eared. Ruth lay prone on the floor, the book propped up on the fender, studying intently a photograph of a blurry-faced woman riding a horse. The caption to the photograph read: 'This picture shows the horse pushed evenly into the trot by the rider's leg-aids and seat. Note the happy look of the horse, and the true movements of the diagonal legs (the off-fore and near-hind on the ground, whilst the near-fore and off-hind have simul-taneously left the ground). Compare with plates 16, 17 and 18.'

'Dinner's ready,' her mother said. 'Get up off the floor, Ruth. It's draughty.'

'It isn't,' Ruth said.

Her seventeen-year-old brother, Ted, home from work for the dinner-hour, peered over her shoulder, grinning. Ruth put her hand over the book. Ted sat down at the dinner-table and as Ruth got up to join him he said, 'Note the happy look of the child, and the true movements of her diagonal legs as she crosses the floor.'

1

Ruth scowled furiously.

'Sitting down on her well-rounded hind quarters, she picks up the fork with her near-fore—'

'Ted, give over,' said his mother.

Ted said, not teasing any more, 'I passed a lot of kids dashing about on ponies on the way home. In a big field. Pony Club Trials or something. There was a notice up.'

Ruth looked up avidly. 'Where? Near here?'

'Brierley way. Jumping and all that.'

'Oh!' Ruth's scowl vanished and her face became all passionate anxiety. 'If I'd known!' She glanced at the clock. 'Do you think it'll still be on? If I go—'

'I'll drop you there on the way back to work if you like.'

'Yes, of course! Oh, yes, I could!'

Her mother looked at her doubtfully. 'How are you going to get home?'

'Oh, I'll walk or find a bus or something.'

'If you find a bus round these God-forsaken parts you'll be lucky,' Mrs. Hollis said with a sniff.

But Ruth had no thought for afterwards. To get there was all that possessed her. She ate hurriedly, taking no notice of her mother's disapproval. Her mother was disapproving by nature, and did not like the new place they had come to live in, which had made her more disapproving still. Mr. Hollis, a born optimist and peacemaker, said she would get used to it, but Mrs. Hollis said how could she get used to only three shops, five miles to any more and three buses a day to get there? Their house was in the middle of a new 'development of Sunny, Spacious Homes' that had been grafted somewhat incongruously on to the edge of an untidy village in East Anglia. The Sunnyside Estate had a concrete road and concrete lamp-posts and open-plan front gardens, but the rest of the village had gritty tarmac full of pot-holes, or mere mud, and gardens overgrown with gnarled pear trees

2

and sour apples.

'The sooner you go back to school the better,' Mrs. Hollis said to Ruth. 'Moping round all day with nothing to do.'

'But I have something to do now,' Ruth pointed out. She did not like her new school much.

'Hmm,' said Mrs. Hollis.

Ruth finished her pudding and said to Ted, 'Can we go now?'

'Oh, give me a chance,' Ted said, but pushed his chair back from the table in a hopeful manner. 'The old sausages have got to meet the digestive juices.'

'I'll get ready,' Ruth said. She did not want her mother or Ted to see how excited she felt, and she knew it showed. She walked nonchalantly out of the room. She could feel the hot pounding of her joy in her inside: a great flushing of gorgeous anticipation. The unexpectedness of it unnerved her; usually such days, like the never-to-be-forgotten day at the Horse of the Year Show at Wembley, and the day at the Royal Windsor two years ago, were ringed on a calendar weeks before, and approached with a maximum of anticipatory sensation—so great at times as to make her feel sick and almost incapacitate her for the great moment. Her father told her she cared too much. 'Nothing matters that much,' he said to her quite often. But wanting a pony did. Ruth used to cry in bed at night after going to a horse show, because she did not have a pony. 'When we go to live in the country, perhaps you can have a pony,' her father had said. They had lived in the country for two months now, but he had not said any more about it. Ruth wanted to ask him, but she was so frightened that he would dash her hopes that she did not dare to. She was afraid it had just been a prevaricating thing to say, and that if she asked again he would think of something else, like not being able to afford it. But soon she would ask him, Ruth thought, because it was all she thought about. She was nearly twelve, and soon it might be too late:

she would grow too tall and need a horse that would certainly eat too much for her father to afford. According to a book Ruth had (a very old one that her father had bought in a junk-shop), people should start riding at ten. If you did not learn to ride as a child you would never acquire a good seat, it said, unless you joined the cavalry and received military training. Ruth realized there was no possibility of her ever joining the cavalry—she wondered if there was such a thing as a mounted police*woman*?—and meanwhile, as far as she could see, her life was being wasted. If she were to say that to her father, he would laugh and say she had no sense of humour. 'Well, I haven't,' Ruth thought. Her only consolation was that, for her age, she was small and thin. Pony-sized for a few years yet.

She pulled her anorak off the hook on her bedroom door. She was already wearing jeans and a blue polo-necked jersey, so getting ready did not take long. Ted started putting on his motor-bike clothes. Ruth fetched the old crash-helmet she wore when she rode pillion, and her mother gave her her bus fare home. '*If* you can find a bus,' she said, 'which I doubt. Now, mind how you go, Ted. You're not in a hurry.'

It was cold on the back of the motor bike. Ruth pressed up close to Ted, her thumbs hooked in his belt, her nose full of the oily smell of his coat. The bike crackled through the village, bounced over the level-crossing, then roared away with the ear-splitting din that Ted loved up the hill and into the country. Through streaming eyes, Ruth saw the Friesian cows, the bare elms and the rolling pastures that fell away to the flat, ditch-seamed marshes and the shining thread of the tidal river. She grinned into Ted's coat, for having come to live in such a place, after London. She saw herself riding along the sea-walls on her pony, a gleaming, eager little beast, ears pricked up, the wind in his tail . . .

4

'Oh, I must!' she said into Ted's coat.

After some twenty minutes of wild swooping along narrow lanes, Ted turned and shouted something. He was slowing down. Ruth lifted her head and peered over his shoulder. She saw a flag flying at the gateway of a field, purple, pale blue, and gold, and in the field a lot of ponies being ridden, and horse-boxes parked in a row by the hedge.

'Here you are,' said Ted, pulling up by the gate. 'All right?'

'Yes.' Ruth got off, shivering.

'I'll look out for you on the way home, in case you're still walking.'

'I'll manage,' Ruth said. She pulled off her crash-helmet. 'Here, what shall I do with this?' She looked round in dismay. Nothing would have induced her to enter the field wearing anything as inappropriate as a motor-bike helmet. 'Can't you take it?'

'I can't wear two, can I? Stick it in the hedge. Don't leave it behind, though. Cheerio.'

With a blast of noise he was gone. Ruth, nervously fumbling the helmet, walked through the gate. There was nobody to take any money, or tell her to go away; nobody took any notice of her at all. The field was huge and open, on the top of a hill, and the cold Easter wind swept it. All the adults Ruth could see wore suede coats with sheepskin linings, but they looked cold, and stamped their feet. An enclosure was roped off not far from the gate, which Ruth took to be a collecting-ring, for it was full of ponies and riders, standing or walking about, and from it at intervals a pony would go out and a loudspeaker would give its name and number, and the name of its rider. It would then canter off across the field, jump (or refuse to jump) some rails into an adjoining field, and canter away up this field to disappear over a brush jump and into a wood in the middle distance.

'It's Hunter Trials,' Ruth decided.

She surreptitiously hid the crash-helmet in the hedge, and walked over to the collecting-ring, shivering with cold and excitement. She half expected to be told to leave by one of the cold adults, but she was ignored. The girls on the ponies looked at her without expression. This suited Ruth very well. She did not want to be noticed. She only wanted to look at the ponies.

The ponies were a mixed bag. Quite a few of them, when it was their turn, cantered stickily away from the collecting-ring, refused the first jump three times, and then, on being eliminated, cantered eagerly back to their friends. Ruth's heart bled for their riders, who tried not to look as if they minded. 'If I had a pony,' she thought, 'he would jump that jump.' She was sure she could make him. It was an easy one. She pushed her cold hands into her anorak pockets, and saw herself galloping up the hill towards the wood. 'Like that,' she said to herself, when a boy on a flaxen-maned chestnut did as she would do. The pony went like a tongue of flame over the bright grass. The girls in the collecting-ring watched him, scowling. Ruth heard one of them say, 'Oh, that Peter McNair!'

Peter McNair was better than any of the girls. His pony (Toadhill Flax, according to a programme Ruth caught blowing across the grass) was a Welsh cob with cream feather, like an Agincourt charger, and a white mane that fell down to his shoulder. The course was over two miles long, and the middle part ran through a wood that straggled down the valley just below the collecting-ring. The ponies had to go through it at the top, out into the country and back into it at the bottom before the fast finish over two of the big fences left over from the point-to-point, but squished down in the middle with regard for the smaller animals. Ruth watched Peter McNair disappear at the top end, and ran down across the grass to the bottom end of the wood to watch him come through. There was nobody there except a woman on a folding chair, taking the score, and stamping her feet in the leaf-mould. She took no notice of Ruth, who stationed herself where the course came out of the wood. The way in was through a gate, which had to be opened and closed again, through some trees and over a stream, then round over a log, over the stream again and immediately up a steep muddy bank and out over a rail at the top.

'Tricky,' Ruth thought, imagining. Most of the competitors got off for the gate, but Peter McNair did it all from the saddle. Toadhill Flax skidded to a halt alongside, tearing great streamers out of the grass, and his rider leant down and pulled off the loop of string. The pony, having covered most of the last one and a half miles at a gallop, danced through, quivering with excitement, but Peter McNair held him with one hand, and turned him with his legs, and got him to stand while he dropped the string back. Ruth, watching, thought it was done by magic. Everyone else had had terrible trouble with the gate, pulling their ponies through, and then not being able to get near enough to shut it again, or not being able to remount for the whirling of the excited pony. But Toadhill Flax, as if held on a thread, trembling with excitement, pivoted on his forehand for Peter McNair to put the string back. The cold wind tossed through the wood. Ruth shivered, her eyes riveted on the beauty of Toadhill Flax. She saw Peter McNair just then, easing the chestnut so that from his quivering immobility he leapt into life again, with a great churning of mud, down the bank and over the stream. Instantly he was caught up, to trot neatly through the trees, over the log, and back to the stream, beautifully in hand. Peter McNair pressed him on then, three strides from the stream, and he was over it with a fine stretch and a lifting of the white mane, and up the bank

7

like a trained commando, his rider well forward and with him, ready for the awkward rail at the top. 'Up, Toad!' Peter McNair shouted, and Toad jumped, neat as a cat, springing from his muscled hocks, his tail streaming in the wind. Then out into the open again, at a flat gallop. Ruth ran after them, to watch them finish, entranced by the display of perfect control. 'That's how I would do it,' she said to herself. And, even though her father said she had no sense of humour, she grinned, mocking herself. 'Ruth McNair Hollis,' she thought, 'on Sunnyside Semi-Detached ... Oh, how can I ever? Without a pony at all?'

Peter McNair, at close quarters, was rather a disappointment. Ruth went back to the collecting-ring, and stared at him. Toadhill Flax stood impatiently, jiggling his quarters and snorting out through wide red nostrils, but Peter McNair just sat without looking excited at all, not speaking to anyone. He looked (was it possible? Ruth thought) bored. He was about the same age as herself, or a little older, a stocky boy, sandy fair. He looked at Ruth, and through her, without his expression changing. Ruth looked at his pony, and thought she would never see another animal as lovely as Toadhill Flax. He was all spring and spirit, yet stood obediently, mouthing his snaffle. When Peter McNair went to get his red rosette, the pony looked more handsome than ever, the red silk clashing against his chestnut, its forked tails fluttering beside the big, inquisitive eye.

The last class was for jumping the course in pairs. Ruth, not missing anything, watched Peter McNair ride across to the girl who had come second to him and ask her if she would ride with him.

'I can't. I'm entered with Jill,' the girl said.

'Jill could find someone else,' the boy said.

Ruth saw the girl with the blue rosette hesitate. But before she could say anything, a girl on a grey pony said, 'Jane, you wouldn't! Just to give the McNairs another rosette!' And she looked at Peter with angry green eyes. 'Cat's eyes,' thought Ruth, fascinated. Peter flushed slightly, but grinned.

'Will you?' he said to Jane.

Ruth watched Jane being sorely tempted. A whole range of expressions ran over her face, from excitement to doubt. But she caught the cat's eyes of the girl on the grey pony, and shook her head.

'It's not fair,' she said. 'No.'

'Good for you,' said Cat's Eyes. She looked mockingly at Peter, and said, 'I'll pair with you, if you like.' Ruth recalled that her grey, a fat gelding with sleepy eyes, had refused three times at the first fence and been eliminated. Peter, obviously not easily ruffled, said, 'Thanks for the offer, which I take great pleasure in refusing.' He wheeled the chestnut round and trotted away towards the row of horse-boxes.

'There!' said Cat's Eyes. 'What a nerve! Typical McNair. He's going home now. Talk about sporting spirit!'

'Oh, well. He can't help it, I suppose.'

'I feel rather sorry for him, in a way,' said Cat's Eyes, maddeningly complacent. Ruth disliked her. 'Anyone could win with the McNair stable to choose from.'

But Ruth, remembering how the boy had ridden the champing chestnut through the gate, holding his electric power with such tact, and skill, did not agree. She did not think Cat's Eyes could have ridden Toadhill Flax through the gate, over the stream and up the bank without hitting the rail, and not lost any marks.

But the intrigue passed, the pairs jumped, the rosettes were awarded. The judges were collected from the far parts of the course by Land-Rover; and the horse-boxes, and strings of riders without horse-boxes, started to filter out through the gate. The cold wind was still blowing, and the grass showed the way the ponies had gone, but the field was empty. There was rain on the wind now, almost sleet. Ruth realized that she was frozen. She turned her head up into the wind, and her black hair blew back from her face. The wine-warmth of joy had dissolved, and she was left with the old familiar ache that would have her crying later, when she was in bed.

'Oh, I *must*—' she said out loud, into the wind.

She turned round, her eyes picking out the jumps. She was alone in the field now.

'I don't want to win,' she said. 'Only to get round, on my own pony.'

She shivered, hunched against the wind. 'I will,' she said to herself. 'I will. It isn't asking anything much.'

But she knew, to her, it was.

thought, 'buy a pony? Not *knowing*?' She was determined now to have a pony. She would not postpone asking any longer. But she knew she could never be one of those casual girls who took it all for granted.

Her mother was right about the buses. There weren't any. Ruth, her head full of ponies, did not mind walking, at first. She was in a complete dream, and did not notice anything. She was thinking about their back garden, which would have to be their paddock, and wondering, as she had wondered many times already, whether it would be big enough. Their 'Sunny Spacious Home' was on a corner of the estate, and had a bigger garden than all the rest, a big awkward triangle. Nobody in their house liked gardening, so it was still all wild and full of half-bricks and lumps of breeze block. Fortunately, being in the far corner of the estate, it backed on to a field, instead of somebody else's back garden, and there were big trees in the hedge which gave a bit of shelter. For there would be no stable for Ruth's pony. No luxuries, Ruth thought. Just the bare pony, if she were lucky.

'I will ask Dad tonight,' she said to herself. Anything would be better than just thinking about it, and being afraid to ask. She wished desperately that her father was a farmer, who would say, 'Of course, lass, you can keep it in Ten Acre. I'll pick you up a useful animal in the market on Friday,' instead of a traveller for Tibbett's Toilet Ware, who would go grave at the thought of spending money and say, 'Ponies don't live on air, you know.'

Ruth walked along thinking about buying a pony. She had forty pounds in National Savings Certificates. Her brother Ted had had sixty pounds, and had taken it all out to buy his motor bike three months ago. It started to rain again, and Ruth plodded on, head down. She pulled the hood of her anorak up and put the crash-helmet on top. There was nobody to see, as she was on a deserted stretch of country lane which

12

ran, undulating, between vast fields whose hedges had been cut out. 'The sort of farmer I don't like,' Ruth thought. It was efficient but ugly. In the burnt-out ditches the rain-water reflected the black grass. The rain started to hurt, with sleet in it, driving horizontally across the bleak lane, and Ruth put her head down against it. Her wet jeans plastered themselves to her legs and the sleet tinned on her helmet. There was nowhere to shelter, not even a tree, so she just had to keep on walking.

After a few minutes she heard the noise of a heavy lorry approaching from behind. She shifted over into the verge, glancing over her shoulder. It was a big horse-box, with 'McNair' painted over the cab. It went past, soaking her still further with spray from its wheels, but about twenty yards farther on it stopped. She walked on. The door opened and a man put his head out into the rain and called back to her, 'Want a lift?'

'Oh, yes, please!'

Ruth ran, and scrambled up into the seat beside the driver. The cab was hot and fumy, with steam on the windows, deliciously comfortable. She slammed the door.

The man put the lorry in gear and eased it into motion once more, and said, 'I don't pick anyone up as a rule, but on a day like this . . .' He grinned. 'Bit wet, aren't you?'

'Yes.'

'Where are you going?'

'Wychwood.'

'I can put you down there, then. I pass it. Bit of luck for you, eh?'

'Yes, I thought there would be a bus, but there wasn't. I went to watch the Pony Club Trials.'

'That's where I've been. Left at three, but had to take young Peter up to Potton to ride some ponies his father's thinking of buying.'

'What's his father, then? A dealer or something?'

'Yes. You not heard of McNair? It's quite a business he runs, him and the three boys. The two eldest do a lot of racing now, and jumping. Young Peter has to handle the ponies—the others have got too big. They work hard between them—the old boy's a right slave-driver. Wouldn't have got where he is if he wasn't.'

'Have you got Toadhill Flax in the back, then?'

'Yes, that's right. You saw him jumping, eh?'

'Yes. He's a gorgeous pony.'

'Flashy. Done well, hasn't he? Six months ago that pony was as wild as they come, straight up from Wales. And yet today he went round that course and beat the lot of them. That's McNair for you. Work! He never stops. Get a colt like that for twenty quid at the sales, and a year later it's worth two hundred.'

'How does he do that, then?'

'Sheer hard work. Those boys—they're in the stable at six every morning. Peter now—he'd work young Toad (he calls him Toad—says he jumps like a toad) before school, and again when he comes home. Every day. Steady. The old man shouting at him—got a temper like the devil himself, has the old man, but only with people. I've never heard him raise his voice to a horse. He's a right character, I can tell you. Fair, too. You won't get a bargain off him, but he'll not cheat you. He'll not cover faults up. And if he doesn't think you're fit to have a horse of his, he'll tell you straight. Doesn't mind what he says. But work! Cor, he doesn't know what it is to sit in front of a telly. People like that—they deserve to make money, by my reckoning. Good luck to 'em, I say.'

Ruth began to understand what the girls had meant with their sideways remarks about the McNair establishment. No wonder Peter could ride . . . even Cat's Eyes saying she felt rather sorry for him made sense now. Ruth wondered (knowing how she felt herself when she first opened her eyes in the morning) whether Peter McNair really wanted to get up at six every day, to be shouted at by his father.

'I want to buy a pony,' Ruth confided to the cheerful driver.

'Come and see McNair, then. You won't be sorry. He's got some nice little animals, just suit you. We're only three miles farther on from Wychwood. On the Hillingdon road. It's on the right, set back a bit, but there's a notice on the road marking the drive. You can't miss it.'

Ruth, in the steamy cabin of the horse-box, hypnotized by the windscreen wipers diverting the deluge of rain out of her vision, sank into a happy dream of herself buying a pony from Mr. McNair. Having him trotted out . . . running her hands down his legs, like the people in books . . . looking knowledgeably into his mouth. Every now and then from behind the partition she heard a snuffle or the clonk of a hoof from Toadhill Flax, and for a few minutes she had a sense of belonging to the horse world, swishing through the rain with the warm smell of horse permeating the cabin. 'It's lovely,' she thought. 'I am happy.'

'Here you are,' said the driver. 'I'll have to drop you here. I go straight on.'

The dream was over. 'Thank you very much.'

She walked home, head down against the rain.

'Oh, Ruth! What a sight!' said her mother. 'I wondered whatever you could be doing, this weather! Did you find a bus?'

'No, there wasn't one. I walked a long way, then a horse-box stopped and gave me a lift.'

'A lift, eh? What have I told you about taking lifts?' her mother asked crossly.

'Oh, Mother, in this weather, surely? Besides, I told you,

it was a horse-box.'

'With a horse driving, I suppose?' Mrs. Hollis said tartly. 'Because it was a horse-box, that makes it all right?'

'Yes,' said Ruth.

'Sometimes, Ruth, I think you're plain stupid,' her mother said. 'Go and get changed and put those wet clothes on the washing-machine.'

'Do you think Daddy will say I can have a pony now? He said we could when we lived in the country. Do you think, if I ask him . . . ?'

'There's no harm in asking. But don't expect too much. This house is about all we can afford at the moment. The mortgage is over five pounds a week. Where do you think it all comes from?'

Ruth shivered, and went upstairs to change. 'I will have one,' she said to herself. 'I will earn some money myself. I'll work in a shop on Saturdays. Or do a paper round. Or—' She couldn't think of anything else. 'If not I shall die.'

She took her wet clothes downstairs and dumped them in the kitchen. Her mother, smart in towny shoes and a frilly apron, was cutting up tomatoes. Ruth thought gloomily, 'She'd never sit all day on a little stool in a wood scoring marks for a Hunter Trials. She doesn't understand anything about what matters.' She felt uncomfortable thinking such things, but the thoughts came nevertheless. Ruth wanted a tweed mother, with pony-nuts in her pockets.

Ted came in, and later her father drove his car—or, rather, Tibbett's car—into the drive and stamped his feet on the doormat, sniffing the kitchen smells. They all sat down to supper and Ruth ate without noticing, only thinking of what she had to ask her father. 'Tonight I will know, one way or the other,' she thought, and felt sick. She could not get the question out. Her father finished his meal and sat on with a cup of tea and the evening paper. Ted went out. Mrs.

Hollis started washing-up, and Ruth had to clear away. She felt cold in her stomach, and the question would not get past her lips. There was a pencil on the table, and she sprawled in a chair opposite her father, drawing a horse on the formica.

'Ruth, for heaven's sake!' Her mother swooped down with a cloth.

'Can I have a pony?' Ruth said desperately.

'Pour me another cup of tea,' her father said, pushing his teacup out from round the newspaper. Mrs. Hollis took the cup.

'Ruth's on about this pony business again,' she said. 'You'd better settle it one way or the other, John, else we'll get no peace.'

'Oh.' John Hollis lowered the paper reluctantly. 'What is it, then?' He knew perfectly well.

'Please can I have a pony? You said I could when we lived in the country.' Ruth looked at him, quivering.

He frowned. 'Well . . .'

'Please. I shan't ever ask for anything else. Not clothes or anything. If I can just have a pony. I'll look after it and everything. You won't have to do anything.'

'Only pay for it,' said her father.

'I'll earn some money. I'll do a paper round. Mary Barker does one, and they want another—there's a card in the shop. I promise. And I could use my National Savings. Ted did for his bike, so there's no reason why I shouldn't. I've got forty pounds.'

'Oh. Would that buy a pony?'

'I don't know. I should think so. I could find out.'

'But then you have to feed it when you've got it. How much is that a week?'

'Nothing in the summer and only hay in the winter. And hay's cheap in the country, almost nothing,' Ruth said recklessly.

'Where would it go?'

'Out the back. There's enough. You wouldn't have to do any gardening. He'd graze it all smooth and it would look lovely.'

'It sounds a lot too simple the way you put it,' her father said, half serious, half smiling.

'Well . . .' Ruth smiled too, uneasily.

'How do you go about it, then? Buying a pony, I mean. You have to know something about it, don't you? Do you know enough?'

Ruth knelt on the chair, thin eager-elbows on the table. 'I met a man today, the man who picked me up in the horse-box, and he works for a Mr. McNair who lives on the Hillingdon road, and he's a dealer. Very straightforward, the man said. He said I'd get a good pony from him. I could go and see him, couldn't I? I mean, it's like a shop. You just go and look round and get an idea. Could I go?'

'You never get a bargain off a dealer.'

'I could look at the adverts. *Could* I look, though? If I *found* one, could I have it? It's no good looking if I can't have one anyway. But if you say I can *look* . . .' Ruth's words tumbled out in a heap. 'If you say I can use my National Savings money, then I could look, couldn't I? Ted used his.'

'Well, his motor bike was for getting to work on. Not just pleasure.'

'Oh, it *is* pleasure!' Ruth said. 'You've only got to look at him—'

Her father grinned. 'He had a wonderful argument for buying it, though. Better than yours, my girl.' But he was too kind to tease her further. 'All right. You use it. In ten years' time it won't be worth much anyway, and as you're so set on this idea I won't say no. You can go shopping.'

'Tomorrow?'

'Tomorrow. Looking. If you find anything hopeful, you must report home. And don't look too keen.'

18

'*Oh!*' Ruth was speechless with excitement. Her face went red, and then white, her lips quivered. Her father looked at her, and said, 'You are a funny girl.'

Mrs. Hollis picked up the empty teacup. 'While you're in a decision-making frame of mind, dear, how do you feel about my putting my name down with the Council again? We're well settled in now, and I'd like a child about the place again.'

When they had lived in London, Mrs. Hollis had been on the local council's list of foster-mothers, and a succession of small children, one at a time, or occasionally two, had followed each other in the Hollises' spare bedroom. They were children whose mothers had had to go to hospital, or occasionally whose fathers were in prison, or whose parents had been evicted; normally they had not stayed for more than a few months. Just long enough, Ruth had often thought, to get so that they were one of the family. Then, when they went, it was a wrench and a misery; she did not like it.

Het father said, 'All right, dear. If you want to. But past the crying-in-the-middle-of-the-night stage, please. Sixish, say. Tell them your husband is very sensitive.'

'Well, you take what you're sent as a rule. But I'll do my best.'

'Right. Everybody happy?' Mr. Hollis grinned at Ruth. She was sitting in a dream, staring into space. She did not even hear him. Mr. Hollis looked at his wife and shook his head.

'She'll come down to earth,' Mrs. Hollis said. 'When this pony is a reality. It might not be all bliss—all roses. She'll learn.'

But Ruth, if she heard, would not have believed her.

3 The Forty-Pound Pony

Ruth cycled slowly up the driveway that led to McNair's. She wished it was longer than it was, for she was dry-mouthed with nervousness. The great moment had arrived, but perversely she felt no joy: she was too frightened. It meant so much, and she knew so little. Reading her old-fashioned horse-books by the light of a torch most of the night before had done nothing to help. Her head reeled with the fatal diseases of the horse, imperceptible to the in-experienced eye; with the vices that meant doom: from bolt-ing to wind-sucking. She had read about dealers who filed their horses' teeth to pass them off as youngsters, and dealers who injected their horses with sedatives when prospective buyers were trying them out. 'No foot, no horse,' was an adage to remember, and, from the feet up, the possible blemishes were legion: curbs, splints, spavins, thorough-pins, windgalls and sidebones on the legs alone. Expressive words with ominous meanings floated through her brain: stargazer, daisy-cutter, herring-gutted, Roman-nosed, ewe-necked, cow-hocked . . . She pressed down on the pedals, standing up, as the gravel bogged her tyres. 'I don't know anything,' she thought in a panic, 'only words.'

But now she was in a yard, meticulously tidy, surrounded with loose-boxes, like a photograph captioned 'A desirable layout.' The loose-boxes were new and smart, with concrete forecourts. At one side was a wooden chalet labelled 'Office'; beyond, behind the stableyard, the roof of a large modern house stuck up. Ruth put her bike against the nearest wall, where it looked very untidy, and went to the door marked 'Office'. Before she got there a man came round a corner from the direction of the house, and Ruth stopped short, feeling like a burglar. Mr. McNair, she thought. He was what Ted would have called very hacking-jacket. He said, 'Can I help you?'

Ruth took a deep breath. 'I want to buy a pony.' Her voice sounded very peculiar.

McNair looked at her carefully. He was smart, almost dapper, in a tweed jacket and well-pressed trousers. His expression was non-committal, his eyes shrewd. He had grey hair and hard, working hands.

'For yourself?'

'Yes.'

'About thirteen hands? Thirteen-two perhaps. How well do you ride?'

'I can't really.'

He smiled. 'That's honest. Mostly they say, "Oh, I can

ride," as if the question is an insult. About ten per cent of them can, after a fashion.'

Ruth felt better. If he appreciated honesty, he must be honest with her, surely?

'What do you want it for?' McNair asked. 'Wembley? Or just to keep the grass down at home?'

'Oh, the grass,' Ruth said hastily. Mr. McNair was smiling, but she didn't notice. She was beginning to think that Mr. McNair's ponies might cost more than forty pounds. Everything was so new and expensive, from Mr. McNair's trousers to the first shining bolt that he was pulling back on loose-box 12. There was no rust at Mr. McNair's, no chipped paint, no dirty straw blowing in the evening breeze. Only perfection. Ruth remembered Peter, holding Toadhill Flax on a quivering rein, while he dropped the string. Perfection. 'This isn't my sort of place,' Ruth thought, and in her imagination she saw a stableyard, slightly untidy, with dipping tiled roofs and pigeons, and loose-boxes converted from the old carriage-horse stalls, with cobbles, and cats, and a faithful head looking over the half-door . . . the sort in books. She swallowed desperately.

'Pennyroyal,' Mr. McNair said. 'Nice sort. Six years old.'

Pennyroyal was a dark liver chestnut with no white on him, save a small star. He had a kind eye, and he gave a friendly knucker. Ruth, trying to hold back, loved him immediately, and felt doom descending. She just looked, speechless.

Mr. McNair smiled again. He ran his hand down the hard muscle of the pony's neck, patted his shoulder, and came out into the yard again.

'I don't tell my customers that my horses are what they're not,' he said. 'I don't tell them they're marvellous. They're not marvellous. I just buy horses I like myself.' He was leading the way to loose-box 7. 'I'm hard to please. I've been buying horses for thirty years now. And for every horse I've bought, I'd say I've looked at twenty. '

None of her horse-books had described to Ruth a dealer like Mr. McNair. She was lost, and she knew it. She was far too frightened now to say that she wanted a pony that only cost forty pounds. She looked into loose-box 7, and saw a grey mare, dappled like a Victorian rocking-horse, with black legs and eyes blue-black like best coal. To Ruth she was perfect, utterly desirable, from the bold glance of her lovely eyes to the tip of her frosty tail.

'Sixpence,' said Mr. McNair.

Ruth, in her nervous state, almost jumped out of her skin. '*Sixpence?*'

'Her name,' said Mr. McNair gently. 'The price is somewhat more.'

'Oh!' Ruth went scarlet with horror at her idiocy.

'She's Welsh mountain. I've got her papers in the office. A bit on the small side for you probably. Not now, of course, but in a year or two she would be. Attractive pony, though.'

'Oh, she's lovely!' Ruth's voice was full of misery.

'Most of the ponies are in the field. I'll get Peter and we'll go and see them.'

They left Sixpence and walked down the row of loose-boxes to a gate which led to the house behind and, presumably, the field. Ruth glimpsed aristocratic heads, honest hunter heads, and the flashy gold beauty of Toadhill Flax. She paused. Mr. McNair said, 'He takes some holding, that one. I wouldn't offer him to a young girl. I'd lose my reputation.'

They went through the gate, which led down between the new house and a newly planted orchard, to another gate at the bottom. As they passed the house, McNair turned his head and bawled, 'Peter!' By the time they got to the bottom Peter McNair was coming down behind them, a couple of halters in his hand. He joined them, leaning on the gate, and nodded to Ruth, but said nothing.

There were about ten ponies in the field, which was large, stretching away to a line of elms on the top of a rise. Some of them raised their heads and looked towards the gate; two walked towards them in a hopeful fashion; one looked, gave a shrill whinny, and galloped away. Against the ridge of the hill, the gallop looked splendid, wild and free, and Ruth watched admiringly.

McNair said, 'Damned animal!'

The pony was a bright bay, not bold in the way of Toadhill Flax, but with an airy, fine action. It seemed to float over the grass. Its gallop set off two or three of the others, but none of them was in earnest like the bay. They wheeled round a few times and went back to grazing. The bay stopped when it was on the horizon, and stood with its head up, watching.

'We made a mistake, turning her out in this field,' Mr. McNair said to Ruth. 'Woodlark, a Dartmoor, T.B. cross. But wild as they come. There's a lot of work there, to make anything of that one. Peter, fetch Sandalwood first.'

Ruth watched Peter walk away across the field, feeling guilty to be causing all this trouble, when she knew now, with a deep-down, horrid certainty, that none of Mr. McNair's ponies cost as little as forty pounds. Half of her longed to enjoy this feast of ponies; the other half trembled with fear at the thought of telling Mr. McNair of her paltry savings. Even when buying things like toothpaste, she did not like to cause the assistant any trouble. She always took the first one she saw, even if she did not like the taste, rather than ask the person to go to any trouble looking. And now here she was, having all this time and trouble spent on her by the exalted McNairs, and it would be to no avail. In silence she watched Peter approach a group of three ponies, talking to them quietly. One came up to him, nuzzling his pockets, but he walked on to a bay that was still grazing, and offered it something out of his pocket. It came up and he haltered it, and one of the other ponies came up, pushing in for a titbit. There was a squeal of jealousy and a great show of teeth and laid-back ears, but Peter disentangled his pony with quiet tact and brought it back to the gate. It was a stocky bay gelding with a thick black mane and tail, a homely pony. Ruth could see him nicely in her back garden, a dependable sort who would go calmly past a dustcart and stop when she fell off. He was not as handsome as the others, but she could love him easily. He looked at her with humble, patient eyes.

'A good beginner's sort,' said Mr. McNair. 'Nothing spectacular, but foolproof. Eight years old.'

'Oh, he's lovely,' Ruth said despairingly.

'Ginny, I think,' McNair said to Peter. 'Then I think that's the lot, at the moment.'

Peter went away and came back with a dark bay mare with a mealy nose and a lot of wild mane. Ruth leaned on the gate, clenching her sticky hands over the top bar, as if she were being tortured. The two ponies stood, heads up, utterly desirable in every way, and she looked at them as if she knew what she was looking for, feeling only this terrible despair, and not able to utter a word of sense. McNair went on talking, but Ruth did not take in what he said. It was no use. They let the ponies go and walked back up to the yard. McNair said, 'Those are the ones that are suitable, just now. In a week or two I may have something else to offer you. We have new ponies in nearly every week.'

Ruth knew it was her turn to say something. They were back in the tidy yard. Peter stood just behind his father, saying nothing, and there was a pointed silence. Mr. McNair looked at Ruth. Gathering up all her courage, and feeling herself going scarlet, she said, 'What—what is the price of—

25

of—' All the ponies' names completely eluded her. The only one she could remember was Toadhill Flax. '—of—them?'

'I could let the bay go for a hundred and twenty. And Ginny, perhaps. The others . . . Pennyroyal, say, a hundred and fifty. He's quite a useful jumper, and is good in gymkhana events. The Welsh mare the same: she's a little winner, and you could get some good foals out of her later.'

Her worst fears confirmed, Ruth felt her scarlet fade, and the cold despair take its place. All her instincts had been right. Not only twice but three times as much as her miserable forty pounds . . .

She said, 'I shall have to ask my father.'

At that moment a large car drove into the yard and Mr. McNair said to Peter, 'Here's Matthews,' and to Ruth, 'Excuse me a moment.' He hurried over to the car and Ruth, grateful to Matthews, whoever he was, was left standing with the silent Peter. Her tumbled emotions no longer disturbed her. It was all useless. She looked down at her feet and mumbled, 'Thank you. I'll go now.'

Politely, still saying nothing, Peter followed her across the yard to where her shabby bicycle was propped against the wall. They passed McNair and his visitor, talking hard on the steps of the office, and McNair called out to Peter as he passed, 'Stay around, Peter. We'll get a saddle on that Woodlark tonight if it's the last thing we do.'

'All right,' Peter said, without any expression.

Ruth picked up her bike. 'Thank you,' she said again, awkwardly. 'Good-bye.'

'I'll come down to the gate. It's supposed to be shut.'

Ruth would rather have shaken off Peter's unforthcoming company, but was obliged to walk on with him down the drive. It then occurred to her that she would never have such an opportunity again to seek advice. At least to Peter she could admit her forty pounds, if not face to face with Mr. McNair.

'Doesn't your father ever have anything cheaper?' she asked him. 'I haven't got that much money.'

'Well—no. Not unless it's very small. There's never anything under eighty.'

'I've only got forty,' Ruth muttered.

'Forty?' Peter's voice was doubtful, but not scornful. 'You'd only get a young pony for forty, an unbroken pony. Or some old crock.'

'A young pony? Like Woodlark, you mean?'

'Oh, heavens, you don't want a pony like Woodlark! She's not worth anything at all. You want a quiet one. Mr. Marks, at Ramsey Heath, has young ponies quite cheap, sometimes. You ought to go and see him.'

'Mr. Marks?' Ruth fastened on the name, with a great uplifting of spirits. 'You mean he might have one for forty?'

'He might. A two-yaer-old. He buys them at the sales, for a sort of hobby. If you get one with a quiet temperament, you ought to be able to manage all right. He lives at Bramhall, the farm on the right past the pub.'

In that instant, Ruth's world was transformed. She turned to Peter with an eager, shining face. 'I shall go and see him. Thank you for telling me. Oh, thank you!'

Peter looked quite surprised. He smiled, which made him look much more human. Ruth noticed that he had freckles, and was quite ordinary, on the ground. She pushed her bike through the gate and he shut it behind her.

'Thank you very much!' she said again, fervently. As she pedalled away down the road, she thought, 'He thinks I'm barmy. But I don't care!' And she started to sing, freewheeling down the hill.

The next evening she pedalled to Bramhall, and found herself jerking down a rutted lane, with high out-of-control hedges on either side and ditches full of stinging-nettles. Bramhall was a collection of ramshackle old buildings, dungheaps and picking hens, hemmed in with elms full of cawing rooks. It looked to Ruth far more like a forty-pound place than McNair's, and she liked it instinctively. She liked the faded rose-red of the stable bricks and the thatch with grass growing out of it, and the sour smell of an early elderberry. She was full of hope. She left her bicycle by the gate, where it looked quite smart, and went into the yard. A youngish man was just shutting three cows into a cowshed. He turned round and looked at her with a cheerful grin.

'I'm looking for Mr. Marks, about buying a pony,' she said.

'I'm Marks,' said the man.

He was not frightening at all, and Ruth was able to say quite easily, 'I want a pony, but I only have forty pounds. Peter McNair said you might have one.'

'Oh, you've been to McNair's, have you? I'll bet Mr. McNair didn't offer you one for under a hundred, eh?'

'No, he didn't.'

'Smart place, McNair's.'

'Yes, very.'

'Somebody has to pay for it.'

'Yes.'

'Let's see what we've got, then, eh? It's for you, is it?'

'Yes.'

'He told you they're only partly broken? You can catch them, and halter them and handle them, but they're only youngsters. Two-year-olds. I got this lot from Beaulieu— the New Forest sales. I got a dozen, last September, but I've sold most of them. There's four left now. They're down in the bottom field. We'll go along. Just a moment.'

28

He went into a shed and fetched a sieve of oats and a halter, and then led the way down a rutted track between more massive rampant hedges. It was a dull day, and Ruth had a sense of the earth, fed on damp, overwhelming Mr. Marks's property with its swaggering growth. The verges were lush with forward grass, the budding branches tossed over their heads with an uncultivated abandon. The gate to the ponies' field was set deep in rampant hawthorn, with gnarled Constable oaks on either side; the field was not very large, and sloped down to a stream and a thick wood full of crows. Ruth was enchanted with the old-fashionedness of it; the lovely scorn of modern clearance, the encouragement of crows and vermin-sheltering hedges. Later, she could see, it would be all knee-high buttercups and cow-parsley, like a Victorian painting. 'There will be a pony here for me,' she thought. 'It is a "me" place. Not like McNair's.' A little shiver of excitement ran through her.

Mr. Marks gave a shout and a whistle, and the four ponies converged upon the gate. They were all rough and muddy and, after McNair's, definitely of a half-price breed. Except for one. Ruth's eyes went past the thick-legged grey, the wall-eyed skewbald and the nondescript black, and rested on the pony that held back from the others. 'That is for me,' she thought.

It was, in fact, nothing special in its looks: a gelding of an unusual bay-roan colour, like a bright bay that had been left out in the frost. His legs were black and his head was dark, with a small crescent of white between the eyes; the forelock was black and the mane grew whiter as it went down towards the withers where the frosty mantle seemed to have fallen most thickly. The stocky quarters were almost pure bay, and the thick tail black. 'Circus pony,' Ruth could almost hear Ted say. But the pony had a look, a presence, a way of standing which made the other three ponies look like cab-horses. He did not come up, but stood behind, head up, watching Ruth.

'Oh, I like that one,' Ruth said.

Mr. Marks gave a grin and said, 'You watch him.'

He started to give each of the other three ponies a handful of oats out of the sieve, and immediately the little bay roan came up, shouldering the black and the skewbald roughly out of the way. His eyes, large and lively, showed no white, only his ears went back with greed and he plunged eagerly for Mr. Marks's hand. The other ponies moved over for him, making jealous faces. Ruth had seen his cocky walk, the firm planting of his round, rather shaggy feet: it was jaunty, sure.

'He's the boss around here,' said Marks, smiling. 'You're our fly boy, eh? Our smart one? That's what we call him, Fly. He's fly all right.'

'Oh.' Ruth was dubious now. What was fly, as an adjective? As a noun, and a name, it was horrid. As a description, it was rather worrying. Did Fly qualify, she wondered, for Peter McNair's stipulation: a quiet temperament?

'Is he—is he all right? I mean, quiet?'

Mr. Marks pursed his lips. 'Well now, if you're looking for a real quiet one, I'd take the skewbald. Or the black. You can do anything with those two.'

Ruth looked at the skewbald and the black. But beside Fly they were nothing ponies. They were nice, because they were ponies; the had gentle, interested faces. But they hadn't got the—the—Ruth groped for a word and could not find it—the *thing* that Fly had. Fly was a character.

'But Fly—he's quiet?' She had to persist.

'He's got no vices. Wouldn't kick or bite you. But he's got more spirit than the others. I reckon he'll be a more lively ride, when you get a saddle on him. I'll be honest with you, you see. If it's really quietness you're looking for, you should have the skewbald or the black.'

But Ruth could no longer consider the skewbald or the black. She knew already that it was going to be Fly. She only wanted Marks to tell her that he wasn't actually bad.

'Is he forty pounds?'

'Well, yes, I suppose so. If you want him that bad. I was asking fifty really. He's a three-year-old, this one. He's ready to be ridden. But I haven't the time to school him myself. It takes too much patience for me. And my kid's too little yet to ride.'

Ruth, having found that Fly, by the nod of her head, could be hers, was suddenly petrified. She stared at him. She looked for all the things in the books, the faults with the strange names, and deficiencies of conformation, the signs of vice, and the indications of dire disease. And Fly stared back at her, four-square on his black hairy legs, and she could see nothing that the books mentioned, only the pony of her heart, as perfect as Shakespeare's bit in all the anthologies, out of 'Venus and Adonis'. 'Oh, I must be sensible!' she thought to herself. And Fly was looking at her boldly as if it was she who had the faults, knock-knees and rickets and pigeon-toes: it was a straight look, with a glint in it. It was not a look to make her feel sensible. It quenched her fright and her doubts.

'Oh, please, I would like him,' she said to Mr. Marks. 'I've only got forty pounds.'

'Well then, we'll call it a deal,' said Mr. Marks comfortably. He did not strike Ruth as a worrier. 'He's a good pony. The vet's seen 'em all and can't find anything wrong, so you'll be all right there.'

Was it that easy, after all? Ruth could hear her heart thudding, as if it had grown into two. She gripped the top bar of the gate, looking at Fly. She saw him going round the

Hunter Trials course at Brierley Hill, and herself sitting easily in the saddle, confident, easy . . . He had bold, wide nostrils, and was wide between the forelegs. But he wasn't common.

'Is—is he New Forest?' she asked Mr. Marks.

'He hasn't any papers,' Marks said. 'But he came from the forest. I'll bring him down your place, if you like—I know a man with a truck. Save you walking along the road. Where do you live?'

'Wychwood. On the new estate.'

They started walking back to the farmyard. Ruth was in a daze. 'I'll have to get my money cashed. It's in National Savings.'

'Tomorrow do you?'

'Oh, yes. But I won't have the money by then. At least, not all of it. I can give you some.'

'No hurry. I'm not worried. What house is it?'

'South View.'

'About six, then.'

'Yes, thank you very much.'

Ruth found she was cycling home. Her head was filled with the image of Fly, standing there with his legs planted out so firmly, the wind in his tail. She thought, 'Fly is a horrid name, if you think of fly like the thing that makes spots over the windows and sits on cream-cakes in the summer. But if you think of Fly as in flying up in the sky, it is a lovely name. He will be that sort of Fly. Fly. Fly-by-Night.' Ruth was pleased with Fly-by-Night. 'He can be Fly, short for Fly-by-Night. In the Hunter Trials he can be down in the catalogue as Fly-by-Night.' Ruth was cycling through the village and up the concrete road of Sunnyside Estate, her eyes seeing nothing.

'I've bought a pony,' she said to her father, who was having his supper.

He looked up. 'Really bought it?'

'Well, I've got to get the money out. But the man doesn't seem to mind about waiting for it. He's bringing the pony tomorrow.'

'Tomorrow!' said Mrs. Hollis, spinning round from the sink. '*Tomorrow*?'

'Yes.'

'Oh, Ruth, surely—' Even her father looked rather annoyed. Her mother was speechless, gesticulating out of the kitchen window. 'Where on earth—?'

Ruth, feeling rather cold, looked out of the kitchen window and remembered that the back-garden, or field, was full of bricks. There was wire-mesh between it and the adjoining two gardens, but nothing round the sides of the house and at the bottom, save a hedge full of holes. She looked at it forlornly, thinking of the lush spring bounty of Mr. Marks's field. Fly would surely find life here a little different.

'Oh, I'll have it all right by tomorrow,' she said.

Her assumption that a fence would grow out of the ground before the following evening made her parents exchange despairing glances. Fortunately at this moment Ted came in with his friend from work, Ron. Ron, like Ted, was seventeen, tall, skinny, and amiable, with a beloved motor bike.

'We're going to work on Ron's camshaft tonight,' Ted said happily.

'I think,' said Mr. Hollis, 'that you're going to build a fence.'

A vast cattle-truck, trailing small clots of dung, laboured up the slight incline to 'South View' and parked incongruously outside.

The driver leaned out of the cab and yelled towards the

house, 'Six cows for Hollis!'

Ruth ran blindly down the drive and into the road. 'It's my pony! The pony from Mr. Marks?'

'That's right, miss,' said the driver, grinning. He let down the back ramp with a crash and shower of straw, and from the depths of the big lorry Fly's dark eyes stared at Ruth, wild and shining.

'I'll get him, miss. He's a bit scared like.' The man went into the lorry and untied Fly's halter. Fly charged for the daylight, his hoofs drumming the wooden floor, pulling the driver with him.

'Hey, hey, steady on, my bold fellow!'

He crashed down the ramp, skidded on the concrete, and pulled up, quivering, nostrils wide, held sharply by the rope halter. A quiet one, Ruth remembered, was what she should have had. No animal that she had ever seen, she thought at that moment, looked less quiet than Fly.

4 Problems

That night, alone in the pock-marked field, Fly-by-Night galloped up and down the makeshift fences, whinnying for his companions. Ruth lay in bed with the pillow over her head so that she would not hear the pitiful noise. When he stopped whinnying she got out of bed to see if he was still there, and saw him standing with his ears pricked up, gazing into the distance, the moonlight washing his frosted back. She kept going to the window, longing to see him grazing, or dozing, but he did not settle. Ruth would have gone out to him, in the cold moonlight, but she knew that her presence made no difference to his behaviour, for she had spent the hours before bedtime trying to soothe him, and he had ignored her, brushing past her in his agitated circling, looking past her with anxious eyes. The neighbours had watched him, amazed, worried about their wire-mesh, and Ruth's parents had shaken their heads and asked her what had possessed her to choose such a mettlesome beast.

'Any trouble and he'll have to go back,' Mrs. Hollis said. 'Thank goodness we haven't paid the man yet.'

'It's all strange to him,' Ruth cried out. 'He'll settle down! He misses the other ponies.'

Shaken with doubts of her own, nothing would now have induced her to admit that Fly was not a wise buy. More than anything her parents could say, the words of Peter McNair, who *knew,* kept repeating themselves in her head: 'If you get a quiet one . . .' But she did not want the grey, or the black, or the piebald. She was possessed by Fly, with his cocky walk and his questing eyes. 'He will be all right,' she said, 'when he's settled down.'

'Tell the man to go and bring this animal's pals,' Ted said, reinforcing his fence hastily with whatever was handy (the dustbin, the clothes-line, two motor tyres, and a wardrobe door that was in the garage), 'before he goes and fetches them himself.'

'He'll be all right in the morning.'

But in the morning Fly was still whinnying, and roaming round the field close by the fences, so that he wore a trodden path. Even to Ruth's eyes the grass in their field did not look very palatable: it was sparse yet, and full of docks. The drinking-water was in an old cistern that Ted had mended with solder. She thought that some hay might occupy the restless pony, and took five shillings out of her money-box, and went on her bicycle to the nearest farm, where a surly old man took her money and dropped a bale on to her handle-bars.

'We ain't got too much ourselves just now.'

'Thank you very much,' Ruth said, full of gratitude for the favour.

She pushed the awkward load home and dropped a precious armload of the stuff on to the ground for Fly. He came up and snuffed it, ate a little, and trampled a lot of it into the mud. Ruth put the rest of the bale into the garage, but when her father came home and put the car in, the hay had to come out. Ruth put it on the porch, by the front door.

'Ruth, for heaven's sake!' her mother said.

'Where else, then?' Ruth asked, in desperation. Her money-box had only another half-crown in it, and the hay was precious. She knew now that she would have to buy a hay-net, and a halter, too, and after that there would be a saddle and bridle, and a dandy-brush, and saddle-soap, and a hoof-pick. And more hay. Fly was still cantering along his track by the wire mesh, and scratching his hind quarters on the posts, which now leaned towards their neighbours' gardens. The neighbours on one side told Mrs. Hollis that they didn't like the whole business.

'He'll settle down,' Ruth said. She was white, and had dark shadows under her eyes. She went down to the paper shop and signed on to deliver papers to Mud Lane and the road down to the creek, an unpopular route because the houses were far apart and a lot had nasty dogs. 'Eleven shillings a week,' the man said.

'Oh, thank you very much,' Ruth said, once more deeply grateful. At least, on eleven shillings a week, Fly could not actually starve. She would wear her thickest trousers, and gum boots, for the dogs.

'Look, really,' Mrs. Hollis said, surveying the motor tyres and the dustbin and the wardrobe door from the front drive, 'we can't go on looking like this. We'll have the estate people on to us. It looks like a slum. You'll have to buy some stakes and wire and make a proper fence.'

The stakes cost half a crown each, and the wire was nearly three pounds a roll. Mr. Hollis bought them, grimly, and handed them over to Ted and Ron to install. Ted had to borrow a sledge-hammer from the builders. That night Ruth was summoned to a serious talk with her father.

'All right, you've got the pony,' he said. 'But it depends on a lot of things, whether we keep it or not. You understand, Ruth, that it's not because I don't want you to have your pleasure. I want it as much as anybody. But it's a hard fact of life that our budget is already stretched to its uttermost limits, and it's only because Ted has started work and things are that much easier that we were able to buy this new house. And the mortgage repayments on this house are going to take all our spare cash for some years to come. In fact,' he added, 'I sometimes wish we'd gone for some old shack down Mud Lane myself—only your mother would never have stood for it. I don't like this millstone round my neck. I wish—oh, but that's beside the point. But you understand what I'm getting at, Ruth? It's not easy, and if we find we have made a mistake, you will just have to take it.'

'Yes, yes,' Ruth said miserably. 'But I will keep him, with my paper round.'

'You're a good kid. But you've just got to know how things are.'

Ruth, quiet and tired, went down into the garden and Fly came up to her, for the first time. She guessed that the change in his life was as much a shock to his system as actually owning a pony was a shock to hers. He stood, and she stroked his neck, and he lipped at her fingers.

'We shall get used to each other,' Ruth said to him. 'And you will be good. You *must* be good,' she added fiercely. She wanted to join the Pony Club and jump round the course at Brierley Hill. She did not want just a rough pony; she wanted a pony that would be obedient to a touch, that would turn on his forehand at a brush of her heel and canter figure-of-eights on the right leg, like a show pony, and jump anything she asked of him, without running out or refusing. Like the ponies in the photographs and diagrams in the horse-books—always beautifully collected, the riders with their knees and elbows in the right places, smiling calmly. She did not know, then, how much she was asking. She only knew that she wanted it, and that she would try. She looked at Fly, at the way he stood, restless, ears pricked up, his rough coat shining over the contours of his muscly shoulders, and she thought, 'I *will* do it. Even if he isn't quiet. I will.' It occurred to her that she could, indeed, start at that very moment, by leading him round the field, and getting him to stop and start when she wanted. Then she remembered that she had not got a halter. 'Not even a halter,' she thought, and all the things she wanted for Fly (expensive items, for all the horse-books agreed that cheap tack was to be deplored) floated in a vision before her eyes, looking like the interior of a saddler's shop, and all her agony came back.

She told herself, 'A halter is only a bit of rope and canvas,' and that evening she made Fly a halter out of some canvas her mother found in her ragbag and a bit of old washing-line that was in the garage. The next day she led Fly round the field, and he was suspicious, but he went, curving his thick mane to the pressure on his nose, snorting delicately. Ruth was entranced.

'He is as good as gold. He did everything I asked him,' she told her mother.

'I thought he just walked round the field. That's what it looked like to me.'

'Yes, that's what I asked him to do.'

Mrs. Hollis gave Ruth a bewildered look, but did not pursue the subject.

Ruth fetched a pencil out of the kitchen drawer and a piece of her mother's writing-paper, and sat down at the kitchen table. She headed her paper 'Things Fly Must Have'.

Underneath she wrote:

Hay
Bridle
Saddle
Dandy-brush
Hoof-pick

Round these five items she put a bracket, and printed 'At Once' beside it. Then underneath she wrote 'Things Fly Must Have When Possible'. This was a long list, in three columns, to get it all on the paper:

Headcollar	Hay-net	Curry comb
Rope for tying up	Feed-bowl	Saddle-soap
Body-brush	Bucket	Neatsfoot oil
Shoes	Stable	Pony-nuts

Its length depressed her slightly. The item 'Stable' she wrote without pressing very hard, so that it was nearly invisible. Its ghostliness seemed appropriate. When her father came in she asked him about the saddle and bridle.

'You see, I can't ride him unless I have a saddle and bridle,' she pointed out.

'Yes, I do see,' her father said. His expression was guarded. 'I think the best thing, Ruth, is if we decide on a sum—say, ten pounds—and you can buy whatever it is you want. The day-by-day things will have to come out of your pocket-money, or your paper round, but I will give you the lump sum to buy the saddle and bridle and suchlike. After all, you used your own money to buy the animal with. Ten pounds—

oh, say twelve. What do you say to that?'

'Oh, thank you!' Ruth said. 'Thank you very much! That will be wonderful.'

The next morning, in a state of nervous excitement, Ruth cycled eight miles to the nearest saddler's shop.

'I want a saddle and a snaffle bridle, for a pony about thirteen hands,' she said to the man, who looked politely in her direction.

'Certainly, madam,' he said. 'I'll show you what we have.'

Ruth looked. The saddles were all golden new, pungent with the sour smell of stiff leather, utterly desirable. She stroked one happily.

'Is this a thirteen-hand one?'

'Sixteen inches,' said the man. 'It should fit a thirteen-hand pony. You can try it, and if it's not suitable you can bring it back and try another.'

'I like this one. I'll try this first,' Ruth said.

She chose stirrup irons to go with it, and leathers to put them on, and a white nylon girth. Then she chose an egg-butt snaffle bit, jointed in the middle, and a bridle with a noseband and a plain browband. The man laid all this shining impedimenta on the counter, and Ruth added a dandy-brush and a hoof-pick.

'Is that all, madam?'

'Yes, for now.'

The man totted some figures up on a bit of paper.

'That will be thirty-nine pounds, twelve and eightpence, madam.'

Ruth, having pulled out the twelve pounds in an envelope that her father had given her, looked at him blankly.

'Thirty-nine pounds . . .?' Her voice faded into incredulity.

'Thirty-nine pounds, twelve shillings and eightpence.'

Ruth opened her mouth, but no words came out. With a

piercing shaft of mathematical clarity, she worked out that the sum the man was quoting her was only seven and fourpence less than she had paid for the pony itself. The man, meanwhile, was looking at her with a severe expression. Ruth looked blankly back at him.

'You—you're—' She thought, for one sweet moment, that he was playing a joke on her, then she looked at his face again, and knew, quite certainly, that he was not.

'I haven't got thirty-nine pounds, twelve and eightpence,' she said flatly. 'I—I didn't know—' She looked desperately at the lovely, gleaming pieces all laid out for her on the counter. 'I—I—how much is just the bridle?'

The man totted up the separate parts and said, 'Four pounds, nineteen and sixpence.'

'I'll take the bridle,' Ruth said. She wanted him to hurry, before she burst into tears. His face was tight and sour. He took the lovely saddle away and put it carefully back on the saddle horse, and hung up the girth and the leathers, and put the irons back on the shelf. Then, slowly, he wrapped up the bridle in brown paper and gummed it with plenty of tape. Ruth gave him a five-pound note and he gave her sixpence back.

'Thank you, madam.'

Ruth took her parcel and ran.

That same evening Elizabeth arrived, from the Council, to live with them. She was a thin, blonde child of six, who took an instant delight at finding a pony in the back garden, and came out to help Ruth while Mrs. Hollis was still talking to the Child Care officer who had brought her. Ruth had been trying to get the bridle on without any success at all. She was just realizing that to accomplish this small task was obviously going to take time and patience. Fly did not, as yet, take kindly to being tied up, so she was obliged to hold him by the halter and at the same time try to put the bridle on. It was plainly impossible. Fly snorted with horror and ran backwards every time she brought the reins up towards his ears, and then she needed both hands to hold him. She realized that, first, she must teach him to stand tied up; then, gradually get him used to the look of the bridle, and the feeling of having the reins passed over his head. Now, having attempted too much, she could see that he was frightened by the new tack.

She stood holding him, stroking his neck, and hung the bridle over the fence out of the way.

'All right, silly. We'll do it very slowly, and you'll get used to it.'

At this point Elizabeth came up and said, 'Can I have a ride?'

Ruth looked at her with interest.

'Are you Elizabeth?' They had learned about the imminent arrival of a child called Elizabeth the day before, when a woman from the Child Care Department had called.

'Yes. Can I have a ride? What's your name?'

'Ruth.'

'Can I have a ride?'

Elizabeth, Ruth decided, was so skinny she must weigh just about nothing at all. Acting on the moment's impulse, she leaned down.

'Put your arms round my neck.'

One hand holding Fly's halter, with the other she scooped up the eager Elizabeth and slid her gently on to Fly's back. He tossed his head and twitched his shoulder muscles as if an insect was worrying him, but otherwise made no move. Elizabeth patted him.

'He's good.'

Ruth grinned.

'He's *wonderful*!' she cried. Had ever 'backing' a pony been

43

so easy? she wondered.

'Go,' said Elizabeth.

'No, not tonight,' Ruth said. She put her arm up and lifted the child down again. 'Tomorrow you can sit on him again. Nobody has ever sat on him before. You are the first person, in all the world, to sit on this pony.'

It was a great privilege, in her eyes, and Elizabeth took it as such, and opened her eyes very wide.

'And again tomorrow?'

'Yes.'

The next day Fly walked round the field with Elizabeth on his back, but it was over a month before Ruth was able to get the bridle on him. It was a week before she could pass the reins up over his head without his running back and looking horrorstruck, and another week before she managed to get the bit between his teeth.

'The books say roll the bit in brown sugar. Or jam,' Ruth said to Elizabeth. 'Go and ask Mummy for some brown sugar.'

Elizabeth disappeared at the gallop and came back with a bowl of sugar and a pot of strawberry jam. Ruth took a dollop of jam out with a finger, wiped it over the bit, and rolled it in the sugar for good measure. Then she held it on the palm of her hand and approached Fly, who was watching with great interest, tied to the fence by a halter. Ruth put the reins over his head, held the headstall in her right hand, in the approved manner, and put the bit under his nose hopefully. Fly clenched his teeth hard. Ruth, feeling very sticky, pushed the bit against his teeth, gently, but most of the jam and sugar now seemed to be on her rather than on the bit. Somehow, Fly managed to take several crafty licks, and still the bit was not between his teeth. The bridle was sticky all over. Elizabeth was sitting on the grass, eating the jam by scooping it out on a finger, as demonstrated by Ruth.

44

Ruth flung the bridle down crossly.

'Oh, he's so stubborn!' she said. She looked at Fly, tied to the fence, and he looked back at her. He arched his neck, licked his lips curiously, and pawed the ground with a neat round hoof. He would stand tied up if she stayed near him, but if she went away he would pull back and whinny and churn about. Ruth would tie him up and potter about where he could see her, or disappear round the side of the garage just for a minute or two. Gradually she persuaded herself that he was improving. Once he pulled the fence out by its roots—Ted's fence—and once the halter broke, but, these crises apart, progress in this direction was fairly satisfactory. But not with the bridle.

'You need a dozen hands,' Ruth said. She picked up the jammy thing and considered it. Then, experimentally, she unbuckled the bit from one side of the headstall. Then the other. She went over to Fly, and put the bridle on over his ears. She pulled his forelock out over the browband, and did up the throatlash. Then she fetched the bit and buckled it on, on one side.

'Fetch the saucer of sugar,' she commanded the willing Elizabeth. 'Hold it up. Higher. That's right.'

With both hands to work with, Ruth eased the bit into the saucer of sugar and slipped it between Fly's teeth before he knew what she was about. She buckled it on to the other side, and stood back, triumphant. Fly mouthed the strange thing on his tongue, bending to it, tossing his head, curious but not frightened. Ruth was elated, warm with achievement. She stood smiling, utterly happy.

'How's the nag?'

Ted's friend, Ron, having called into the kitchen for some rags, paused on his way back to the garage, wiping his oily hands.

'New bridle, then?' he remarked.

'Yes. I bought it a fortnight ago, and this is the first time I've managed to get it on.'

'Sets you back, horse gear,' Ron said. 'Worse than parts for the bike.'

'Oh yes!' Ruth had given up the idea of ever riding on a saddle, since she had discovered that even second-hand saddles were generally more than the whole sum her father had given her. She looked at Ron with interest, wondering how he came to know about the price of what he called horse gear. Nobody in her family knew about it, and she had not dared to tell her father how much he would have to give her if she was to have her saddle. Encouraged by Ron's interest, she told him about her experience in the saddler's.

'Cor, stone me! I know that bloke. Calls you sir. I bet he called you madam, till he found you hadn't any cash?'

'Yes, he did!'

'Sew their saddles with gold thread, at that place,' Ron said. 'Mind you, new ones are never cheap. Lot of work in a saddle.'

'Yes, but what shall I do? I daren't tell my father how much they cost!'

Ron considered, pursing his lips. He had a thin, amiable, rather spotty face, a lot of untidy hair and, like Ted, smelt of motor bikes. He wore filthy jeans and a black leather jacket with various badges stuck to it and had the same sort of bike as Ted, a twin-cylinder 650 c.c. B.S.A. After they had spent a week polishing their camshafts, they used to ride out and have races along the nearest suitable stretch of road. At week-ends, when they weren't tinkering, they would ride out with their gang. When Mrs. Hollis complained about Ted's obsession, her husband would point out that all his friends were pleasant, well-mannered boys, he was never bored, did not break the law (excepting, on occasion, the 70 m.p.h. speed limit) and wasn't it better than girls? Mrs.

46

Hollis would agree, dubiously.

For all these reasons, Ruth was surprised that Ron knew about saddles—apart from bike saddles.

'Reckon I could find you a saddle,' Ron said.

Ruth stared at him, frightened to say anything.

'There used to be one in an old shed, up Mr. Lacey's place. Pony saddle it was. I remember seeing it, when I used to cut his grass. The lawn-mower was in the shed, and the saddle was stuck up in the rafters. I used to live in Wychwood, you know. Down Mud Lane. Two along from Mr. Lacey. That's why I used to cut his grass.' He looked speculatively at Fly. 'Nice pony.'

'Yes.' Ruth let her breath out.

'When I've finished tonight we'll go along, if you like, and see if it's still there.'

'Tonight?'

'Mmm. When I'm through.'

'Oh!' Not only was the bridle actually in Fly's mouth, but on the very same day it seemed as if she was going to acquire a saddle. To Ruth, after several days of getting nowhere at all, it was as if the day was charmed, bewitched. It was a sort of week described in the horoscopes as: 'Try to be patient. The beginning of the week will be full of minor irritations. But Thursday promises to be an outstanding day, bringing good news and the fulfilment of a long-desired ambition.'

'About an hour,' Ron said.

'Yes.'

Ruth danced back to Fly, still mouthing his bit in exactly the way the books said was to be desired. She hugged him round the neck, smelling the heavenly scent of his thick mane in her nostrils.

'Oh, you are lovely! I adore you? You are *good*!'

'Do you want any more jam?' Elizabeth asked.

'Not now.'

'Can I lick the sugar?'

'Yes. Tomorrow, perhaps, you can ride on a proper saddle!'

'Can we use more sugar and jam?'

'Yes, if it helps him take the bit.'

'I like doing it like that.'

Ruth, having very carefully taken the bridle off, giving Fly time to drop the bit, and not pulling it against his teeth, untied him and took off the halter. He walked away across the bare grass, blowing out through his nostrils. Ruth watched him, glowing with a deep satisfaction.

Her deep satisfaction was shattered when her mother saw the state Elizabeth was in, which Ruth had not noticed, but, after a slight unpleasantness, she was able to escape and join the boys in the front drive. Soon she was up on Ron's pillion and they were scrabbling and roaring through the pot-holes of Mud Lane. The lane, overhung with elms, led down to the creek, and a few tatty weatherboarded cottages sat back from it behind overgrown hedges. Mr. Lacey lived in the last one, just before the lane degenerated into a field track, and the marsh grass took over from the last decaying orchard.

'I reckon no one's cut the old boy's grass since I did it last,' Ron commented, when he stopped the bike on the rutted garden path. Ruth's eyes were already straying to the conglomeration of old barns and sheds behind the cottage. 'What a nice place,' she was thinking. 'Like Mr. Marks's. A "me" place.' She could not take to their smart new house, however hard she tried, when she compared it with the romantic wilderness of Mr. Lacey's abode.

Mr. Lacey came out and recognized Ron, and, after some few minutes of reminiscence and inquiry, he issued a very satisfactory invitation to 'Root out what you please, lad. It's all rubbish.' Ron led the way to one of the sheds, skirting banks of stinging-nettles.

'It was this one, as I remember it.'

The shed was gloomy and full of dust drifting through shafts of the late evening sunlight. Ruth crossed both her fingers and prayed silently, gazing into the dust: 'Please, God, let it be there.'

'Ah!' said Ron.

He was climbing up on an old packing-case, reaching up. 'Look, here we are.' There was a shower of cobwebs and woodrot. Ruth sneezed. Ron swung down and held out his prize, smiling. 'Look, it's no showpiece, but it ought to fit.'

Once, many many years ago, Ruth thought, it had been a good saddle. She took it gingerly, afraid it might crumble in her hands. The leather was dry and cracked, the lining split and spewing stuffing. There were leathers and irons, but the leathers were cracked by the buckles beyond repair, and the irons were rusty.

'No girth,' said Ron, 'and the leathers are no good. But it'll come up all right, I'd say. Neatsfoot oil is what it wants. And the lining renewed, and new stuffing. It won't cost you a fortune, though. What do you think?'

'Oh, if it fits . . .' Ruth, examining, began to see that there was hope. She wiped the seat clear of dust with her elbow, and thought she could see the glimmer of a real saddle's rich shine. In her mind she saw it. She longed to start work on it. 'It's wonderful. If it fits—and it looks as if it should—I am sure it could be made all right.' She was full of gratitude again. She hugged the saddle. She saw herself sitting in it, well down, confident, smiling (as in a diagram captioned 'A good general-purpose seat') waiting to go down to the first jump at Brierley Hill. This was her biggest problem solved. She rode home behind Ron, the saddle on one arm, dreaming.

5 The Girl at 'The Place'

Mr. Hollis went down to see Mr. Lacey about the saddle, and came back looking absent-minded.

'Nice place he's got down there. I mean, it's ramshackle, but-well...' He hesistated, considered. 'You could do things with a place like that.'

'Oh, yes!' Ruth agreed avidly. 'All those old sheds you could turn into stables, and all that orchard and field and—'

'Oh, you—!' Her father laughed. But Ruth knew that he was thinking that he would rather have a place like Mr. Lacey's than 'South View' on the Sunnyside Estate. 'There's nothing to do in a new house,' he said, as he settled down to watch the television. Ruth, watching Fly-by-Night searching for grass in the bare plot they called a field, longed for what she called a Lacey-house, with lots of Lacey-grass.

'He'll starve here,' she said to Ron, watching Fly-by-Night. It was summer, and the grass was growing fast, but in the field Fly-by-Night ate it as fast as it grew, and trod it down flat: the field was too small. His summer coat was through, but he was ribby.

'You ought to ask the estate man if you can use the field behind,' Ron said. 'They're going to build on it some time, but not yet awhile. It's doing nothing. Ask him.'

Ruth's eyes opened wide with amazement. She had never thought such a thing possible, and had worried miserably over her lack of grass. She had been taking Fly out in the evenings along the lanes, to eat the verges. She had sat in the cow-parsley, holding the end of the halter, watching him, and worrying. His ribs showing made him look very much a forty-pound pony. On the end of his halter he ate ravenously, pulling at the lush grass, his thick tail switching. Sometimes, when she sat in the grass, she thought she had never worried so much in her life as since she had bought Fly.

'Do you ride him now?' Ron asked.

'Well . . . sort of.'

Ruth looked at the ground, uncomfortably. She had admitted it to no one, but riding Fly-by-Night so far had been a miserable experience. She had cleaned up the saddle and bought a new girth and new leathers, and had accustomed Fly to the feel of it, and to being girthed up. She had got him to accept the bridle, at last, without resorting to jam, and had taught him to stand still while she mounted him. She had then expected to ride off, walking, trotting and cantering to order. But this was where Fly-by-Night's ideas and her own parted company.

'The trouble is, I can't ride,' she said to Ron.

'Well, you'll soon learn, won't you?' Ron said.

'I suppose so.'

'You mean he bucks you off or something?'

'No . . . not really . . .'

It was difficult to explain just what happened when she rode Fly. Every time it was different, so she never knew what to expect. She had got into the habit of leading him down the road and along Mud Lane until she was on her own, in a quiet place, with just the hedges and the trees for company. Then she would mount him.

In her little green book it said, 'He must be encouraged to walk freely forward . . .' According to the book, Ruth would squeeze with her legs and give him plenty of rein, and under her breath, she would pray, 'Please, God, make him do it.' Sometimes Fly would go backwards. The more she squeezed with her legs, the more eagerly would he back, until brought up short by a hedge, or by nearly falling into a ditch. But if he was in what Ruth thought of as his 'freely forward mood' he would leap off as soon as she eased her reins, and continue at as fast a pace as possible. When he did this Ruth had to concentrate on not falling off. She held on to his mane with both hands, and when she thought she had got her balance she would bravely let go to take a pull at the reins. When she did this, Fly would poke his nose in the air and gallop faster than ever. Gaining courage, and getting more desperate. Ruth would pull again, and then again, with all her strength, and the wild progress would generally finish by Fly swerving suddenly to one side or the other, pitching Ruth off over his shoulder. He would then immediately settle down to grazing, and Ruth would lie in the grass, trying not to cry. Not through fear or pain, but with despair.

When, on the rare occasions Fly-by-Night chose to progress at a forward walk, he would proceed on a meandering course to which Ruth's aids would make no difference at all. He would gaze all about him, as if in astonishment at the landscape, and frequently shy violently at nothing at all, so that Ruth often fell off. The only really satisfactory thing about Fly-by-Night, she often thought, was the fact that he did not run away when she fell off. He always started to graze, without even looking for a better bit of grass than that under his feet. Because he's so hungry, Ruth thought.

'It takes a lot of patience, training animals,' Ron said. 'Horses, dogs—people think it can be done overnight. And it can't.'

'No.'

'Training him would be a lot easier if you had another pony to go with him. One that knew. Then this old fellow would just follow along. There's a girl at "The Place" got a pony. She's about your age. Why don't you go and see if she'd give you a hand?'

' "The Place"?'

'Big house opposite the village hall. Pymm, they're called. Father's in beer. Very rich.'

'Oh.' Ron's monosyllabic description was slightly off-putting. She knew 'The Place', but did not know a pony lived there. It was an old house surrounded by belts of thick trees, with wrought-iron gates and a fake gas-lamp.

'You ought to arrange your paper round, so that you can go there. Then you'd meet them. If you're afraid just to walk in, like.'

Ruth looked at Ron admiringly. 'You do have good ideas! I could try that.'

'Oh, I've got it up here.' Ron tapped his head.

'And the field, too. That's a wonderful idea.'

Ron grinned. 'The trouble with you is you don't see the funny side. You make it all matter too much.'

'That's what Daddy says.'

'Looking at you, worrying, no one would say owning that pony was a great joy to you.'

But Ruth, worry or no, could not imagine not owning Fly. She tried, and she thought of all the things she need not worry about, but the picture was one of such bleakness, such a void, an abyss of nothingness, that she could not even consider it.

'It's hard now, and I know I get in despair, but when I think back I can see that I am making a little bit of progress. So as time goes on it will get better and better. Don't you think so?' Ruth wanted reassurance.

'Should do,' Ron said in his amiable way.

'It's so slow, because I'm not very good. I know what I should do, but it's not always very easy to do it.'

'You're a stickler, I'll give you that.'

'The books make it sound so easy.'

'Well, same as books telling you how to take down a motor bike. It's easy, if you just read about it.'

Ruth longed to know the girl Pymm, whose father was in beer. The thought of a friend, a knowing, horsy girl-friend, who would understand her trials and despairs and rare glows of achievement, whom she could ride with and learn with, was a wonderful, warm anticipation. Ruth had made mere acquaintances in the village school, and none was so attractive as to keep her away from Fly-by-Night. Nobody at school rode. But next term, in September, she would be going to the Comprehensive at Hanningham, six miles away, and she thought, with luck, she might meet somebody horsy there.

Fired with Ron's inspirations, she swopped paper rounds by offering the boy who did 'The Place' a shilling a week, and called on the builder to ask if she could use his field. He said, 'Yes, do, dearie. No responsibility taken if he breaks a leg, though, tell your daddy.' He was on the telephone at the time, and spoke to her between conversations to head office, and what meant so much to Ruth meant obviously so little to him that Ruth came out of his office dazed by the ways of the world. That night she cleared a gap into the field and Fly-by-Night galloped through, tail swirling. The field was about an acre in size, with a good hedge all round it. The grass came up to the pony's belly, brushing his thick thighs with its powdery flowers, and Fly grazed avidly. Ruth watched him, filled with the warm happiness that was her reward when things went right.

'Oh, you will get fat and shine,' she said to Fly. 'And be good.'

The bare garden with its ugly bumps and pot-holes and dock leaves and thistles disgusted her.

'Fancy thinking it was good enough,' she thought.

Elizabeth ran down the garden to meet her and Ruth swung her round by the hands. She liked Elizabeth. Now, when everything was right, with Elizabeth laughing and twirling round till they were both giddy, Ruth could see herself jumping round the Hunter Trials course at Brierley Hill, and Fly-by-Night galloping, ears pricked up, and herself riding beautifully, like Peter McNair. 'Oh, Peter McNair,' she thought with a sudden wrench, 'you could show me how to make Fly walk and trot and canter in obedient circles!' She put Elizabeth down, and thought, 'I must find this Pymm girl. I haven't the nerve to go to the McNairs for advice.'

Delivering the papers, it was a week before she set eyes on a Pymm, linger as she might. It was Mrs. Pymm, and she did not look even faintly horsy, as Ruth had hoped, but more like an actress, with dyed blonde hair and tight pink trousers. Ruth was decidedly taken aback and stood on the doorstep clutching the *Daily Mirror* and the *Financial Times* until Mrs. Pymm put out a hand for them.

'Oh, s—sorry.'

Mrs. Pymm gave her a disapproving stare, took her papers and disappeared inside without a word. Four more days passed and Ruth saw no one but an aristocratic Boxer dog. She felt that Ron's idea was not so brilliant after all, and lost interest. In a few more days she would start at the new school. It was September, warm and golden, and she was alone with her problems.

But when she went up the drive of the Pymm residence the following Sunday morning, a girl was coming out of the front door with the Boxer dog. She was about thirteen, but very elegant, with long pale hair, a pale, sad face, honey-coloured jeans and a white blouse. Ruth was instantly conscious of her feet in their dog-proof gum boots and her muddy jeans and shirt, and shifted her paper-sack nervously on her shoulder. The girl made no attempt to communicate, coolly staring, so Ruth was forced to take the initiative, or for ever regret a lost opportunity. Hot with embarrassment, she fumbled over the papers and said, 'Have you got—er, I mean, someone—someone told me you've got a pony?'

'Yes,' said the girl, not smiling.

'Do you—you keep it here?'

'Yes.'

'I—I've got one, too.'

'Oh.'

'The thing is, mine's not—not broken in, really, I—I—' Ruth could feel herself getting hotter and hotter as the Pymm girl went on staring without her expression showing the remotest interest. Only for the sake of Fly-by-Night's salvation could she have risked such an ordeal. She finished desperately, 'I wondered if—if—oh, it's just that I wondered if you had a pony, you might be able to help me.'

Afterwards she realized that an appeal for help was the best way she could have thought of for melting the Pymm sophistication. Even this cool girl was not averse to accepting the role Ruth's plea accorded to her. She noticeably unfroze, said, 'Oh,' again, but quite pleasantly this time, and added, 'My pony's round the back. Do you want to see it?'

'Oh, yes, please!'

Ruth dropped the paper-sack on the front doorstep, quivering with excitement. She had never seen round the back of 'The Place', for the house was hemmed about with ancient shrubberies and big trees in such a way as to give no vistas to the casual visitor. But, on following the girl round the far corner of the house, Ruth was pleasantly surprised to see a big garden reveal itself, all shaved lawn and immaculate rosebeds, and, beyond it, a paddock ringed round with old elms. There was a garage for two cars, a lot of gravelled space, and a rose-brick building that was presumably the old stables, for the Pymm girl led the way towards it.

'It's in here.'

A loose-box door looked out over the yard. Ruth went to the open top-door and looked in. 'It' was a grey mare, old enough to be, in fact, pure white. She looked to Ruth to be an Arab, with her beautiful arched neck and wide-apart eyes. A fine silky mane fell down her shoulder, catching the light as she turned her head; Ruth saw the wide nostrils flicker, the eyes shining. The mare, standing just under fourteen hands, was as lovely an animal as Ruth ever expected to lay eyes on. She gazed at her in speechless admiration.

The Pymm girl stood by the door, her face showing nothing. Ruth gathered herself together, trying not to appear imbecile. She felt herself bursting with hot enthusiasm, but the Pymm girl's unexcitement curbed her.

'Oh, she's beautiful!''

'Yes.'

How could the girl, Ruth wondered, not rave with happiness at owning such a celestial creature? But the face showed no pride or joy, only a slightly sulky boredom. Ruth was baffled.

'Is she an Arab?'

'Yes.'

'What's her name?'

'Milky Way.' The girl grimaced. 'I call her Milly.'

Ruth was shocked. Milly . . . not even Milky. 'Have you had her long?'

'Three years.'

'Do you show her?'

'Sometimes. She always wins. She cost seven hundred pounds, so she should.'

Ruth was silenced. She thought of scruffy little Fly-by-Night, her forty-pound pony, and her problems. A hard knot of obstinacy stiffened her; she had not come to be awed.

'If—if you go for a ride, sometimes, perhaps—perhaps we could go together?'

'I usually ride in the field. But I could come with you, I suppose.'

'I ride down Mud Lane and in the fields down there. I live on the new estate. I shall go down there this afternoon if—if you want to come?'

'I'm going out all day. But I could come this evening, I suppose.' The girl's eyes were a pale yellow-green, wary, slightly suspicious. Ruth did not think she ever smiled. Ruth said, 'Would about six be all right? If you want to come?'

'All right, I'll call for you. Where do you live?'

'South View. It's on the left. Seven houses along.'

Ruth finished her paper round and ran home with great

58

leaps, being Fly-by-Night doing the Hunter Trials. Ron and Ted were sitting in the drive, poring over bits of motor bike.

'I've done it! I've met her! She's coming riding with me!'

'Help! Two of them!' Ted moaned.

'What's she like?' Ron asked.

'Well . . .' Ruth hesitated. 'I don't really know, yet. She's queer.'

'You should have a lot in common, then,' Ted said.

'She's a lot queerer than me. I didn't find out what her name is. Do you know it?'

'Pearl,' Ron said.

'Pearl Pymm? It doesn't go.'

'No. It was a joke in the village—Mrs. Pymm being mother-of-Pearl, I mean.'

'Her pony is gorgeous. She said it cost seven hundred pounds.'

'Only six hundred and sixty more than yours,' said Ted.

'Peanuts,' said Ron.

Ruth got Fly-by-Night ready in plenty of time. She tied him to the fence and groomed him with her dandy-brush (that and a hoof-pick were the only grooming tools she possessed). His winter coat was just beginning to come through, giving him a richer look. The bay shone with the health of a ripe horse-chestnut, and the white hair was silvery as Milky Way's own. Ruth stood back and looked at him, the pride of possession upon her. He jerked on his halter and looked back, all impatience and scorn, his little ears pricked up, one round hoof pawing at the turf. His hoofs were getting long and broken, Ruth noticed, with a pang of anxiety. She had put off getting him shod, because of the money, and because he did very little work on hard surfaces, and also because he was bad at picking his feet up and she was afraid a blacksmith would be impatient with the pair of them for their incompetence. But she thought she would not be able to put off getting him some attention much longer. 'I will ask Pearl,' she decided, and the thought gave her a pleasant shock at knowing, at last, someone to ask.

'The Pearly Queen's arrived.' Ted came round the corner of the garage, grinning widely.

'Oh, help!' Ruth felt panicky, reaching for the bridle that hung on the fence.

'She said she'd wait outside.'

'Go and tell her I won't be a minute.' Fly-by-Night, sensing Ruth's urgency, swung about and trod on Ruth's foot. She swore at him, tears of agony blurring her vision. 'Oh, you beast, you beast! Why aren't you—you—*elegant* like Milky Way?'

She scrabbled for the girths, and Fly turned his head and gave her a sharp nip on the bottom. 'I hate you!' Ruth cried out. 'Oh, you are beastly!' But he followed her meekly enough round the side of the house and into the front garden.

At the sight of Pearl on Milky Way, both Ruth and Fly-by-Night stopped short. If Fly was surprised by the sight of the white mare, Ruth was no less astonished at the vision that was its rider. Pearl only lacked a Union Jack on her breast to be fit for competing in the Olympics: she wore an immaculate black jacket, snow-white breeches fitting like tights, and black boots. Her hair flowed out from under her hat in a pale cascade. She sat indolently, holding the mare's head in so that Milky Way flexed her neck uncomfortably, flicking white drops of foam on to her chest. Ruth felt her mouth drop open, and made an effort to recover herself. But before she could say anything, Fly-by-Night let out a shrill whinny and plunged forward with such force that she was nearly lifted off her feet.

'Idiot!' She was out of the gate and on to the pavement,

Fly churning wildly in circles, letting out frantic whinnies. Milky Way backed away cautiously and Pearl stared politely. Ruth could only hold on, while Fly's hoofs slithered across the concrete road. She could scarcely hold him and felt herself flung about like a dead mouse with a cat. Her hat came down over her eyes, blotting out the vision of Pearl's derisory snigger. Ruth wished she were dead.

'Here, here, you daft pony.' It was Ron who came to her rescue, his oily hand and wiry strength pulling Fly to a heaving standstill in the middle of the road. The pony was shaking all over, and still letting out high-pitched whinnies which brought all the neighbours out into their front gardens to see what was going on. Ruth felt herself going crimson.

Ron said, 'I'll hold him. Get on. Then I'll lead him for a bit, till he settles. Don't worry.'

'Are you sure it's all right?'

'Yes, of course. He's only excited, after being on his own all this time. I won't let go.'

Ruth scrambled into the saddle and fumbled for her stirrups. 'You go in front,' Ron said to Pearl. 'He should follow all right.'

Milky Way moved off, and Fly-by-Night was pulling madly to get behind her. Ruth, hot with shame, sat grimly down in the saddle, her fingers clenched on the reins. She was frightened, not only of what Fly might do, but of what Pearl was thinking. Fly-by-Night's bare hoofs scuttered over the concrete. Ron, in his oily jeans and leather jacket, a spanner sticking out of his back pocket, hung on to the pony's noseband, forcing obedience. They cavorted down the slope and across the main village street, then Pearl turned Milky Way into the quiet opening that was Mud Lane.

'Down here?'

Ruth nodded, sticky with apprehension. 'It's all right,' she said to Ron. 'I'll manage.'

61

'He'll settle,' Ron said somewhat dubiously. He turned and looked at her, and smiled. 'Okay?'

'Mmm.'

Pearl was waiting, watching Ron distastefully. She held the lovely Milky Way on a very tight rein, even when she was walking, and Ruth began to wonder if, after all, Pearl knew a great deal more than she did.

'If you walk on,' she called to Pearl, 'he should follow now.'

'What's the matter with him?' Pearl asked. Still holding the mare on a tight rein, she kicked her with her heels to make her walk on, and the mare did as best she could, over-bent and uncomfortable. Fly-by-Night bounded after her and jiggled along, pressed up close to her quarters, giving little eager whinnies. Milky Way was too well mannered to kick, but laid back her ears. Ruth concentrated on sitting well down in the saddle, ready for a buck or a shy, prepared for the worst. A part of her mind, at the same time, was thinking of the picture the two of them made, like a pony-book photograph captioned in big letters: *'BAD'*. Amidst all her anxiety, this part of her was already grieving, because she could see already that Pearl did not *know*. She was no female equivalent of Peter McNair, which was the role in which Ruth had cast her. In fact, if she had had Milky Way for three years, and still rode her at a walk on a rein so tight that the poor mare could hardly get her head past a vertical position, Ruth guessed that her ignorance was of the permanent kind, an ignorance in her own character, which did not permit her to admit that she did not know anything. This revelation was so great a blow to Ruth that she almost forgot to worry about Fly-by-Night.

'What's wrong with him?' Pearl asked again.

'Nothing's *wrong* with him,' Ruth said. 'He's not used to being ridden in company, that's all. I'm still breaking him in.' If you could call it breaking in, she added to herself. She felt herself wallowing once more in this mire of frustration that was habitually overtaking her, because nothing went according to the books, and the books, for all their value, had no answer for this abyss that existed inside her which was lack of practical experience. Half of her concentration was always fixed on keeping her insecure seat—on herself, in fact. She sighed deeply, almost groaning.

In spite of her fears, Fly-by-Night did not disgrace himself. Anxious to keep as close to Milky Way as possible, he did not gallop headlong across the fields, nor refuse to go at all, for Milky Way was always moving at an impeccable pace just in front of his nose. He followed her avidly, and although it was plain that his schoolboy ardour annoyed her, she did not show her feelings beyond laying back her ears, because she was so well mannered. To Ruth, the ride was memorable more for the behaviour of Milky Way than the behaviour of Fly-by-Night.

Pearl rode badly. She sat well back on the saddle with her feet thrust forward, and held on by the reins. She had Milky Way in a double bridle, and the mare was cramped with discomfort. In spite of the difficulties Pearl provided for her, the mare's manners were faultless. She had obviously been expertly schooled; she moved beautifully, and obeyed Pearl's ham-handed aids with a willingness to please that roused a great pity in Ruth. Ruth could see that the mare would handle on a gossamer rein and quicken to the merest suggestion from the leg, yet Pearl pulled her about with her impatient, yellow-gloved hands and banged on her sides with her shining black boots as if her lovely Arab were some seaside donkey. And the trusting animal docility with which Milky Way accepted this gross treatment grieved Ruth. The mare had been so well schooled that it never crossed her mind to retaliate. She was all anxiety to obey, her dark eyes fretting and unhappy.

Conversation between the two riders was limited by Fly-by-Night's excitement. Ruth had to concentrate, and Pearl maintained the rather superior, cool reserve that Ruth began to realize was her normal manner.

'Do you belong to the Pony Club?' Ruth asked her when Fly chose to go demurely alongside for a few moments.

'Heavens, no,' Pearl replied, with scorn. 'I hunt,' she added, without enthusiasm.

'She doesn't seem to be interested in anything much,' Ruth told Ron when she got home. Pearl baffled her. 'Not even riding. Only she did say she would come out with me again. So that's something.'

'You mean she's horrible, but you'll put up with her for the sake of your pony's education?'

'Something like that, I suppose. Not horrible, but—oh, queer. She seems so bored. And her poor pony. It's so lovely, and she's so—so unfeeling with her.'

'She probably rides because it's the thing to do. And she'll come out with you because she's lonely. Half her boredom is being lonely probably. She never went to the village school, because it's free, and now she goes to some tin-pot private school somewhere miles away, so she doesn't know anybody in the village.'

'She doesn't know much—she's not horsy, in spite of having a pony. In fact, I think she—she's worse than me.'

'Good heavens!' Ron looked appalled, teasing.

'But it was a good idea, all the same. Your idea. I should think Fly will stop being so funny if I go out with them a few times. I mean, I can stand her if he improves. She might improve, too, come to that.'

'Or you might meet someone at the new school.'

'Oh, school!' Ruth grimaced.

That was tomorrow.

6 Slow Progress

When Ruth went to the new school she quickly discovered
that there were no depths of horsy talent waiting to be
plumbed among her new classmates. Four admitted to
having ridden, one on a thirty-year-old Shetland pony, one
on a heifer and two on donkeys. But on her fourth day at
school, standing patiently in assembly while prayers were
read, pretending she was Fly-by-Night, lining up in the
show-ring, mouthing an imaginary bit, she was startled by
the sight of the boy who stepped up beside the head-
master to read the lesson (a dreaded task that she had learnt
was liable to fall on any pupil at any time, forecast only by a

list pinned up on the notice-board every Monday morning). The boy in his navy-blue blazer, red tie, and dark-grey trousers was fair and stocky, and spoke in a flat, untroubled voice which roused Ruth out of her dream. It was Peter McNair.

It was, of course, perfectly natural that he should attend the same school as herself, but the possibility of it had never entered her head. She felt almost stunned by the shock of his incredible appearance before her very eyes, reading the Bible: quite the last occupation she had ever envisaged him at. But after a few days, having become used to seeing him about, she realized that his presence at school was as remote as it had been at the Hunter Trials. He was in the form above her, which mixed with her own class scarcely at all, and, as a boy in a clique of boys, he was hardly likely to want to make friends with a *girl*. From a few discreet inquiries, Ruth discovered that nobody knew that he rode at all. He was a quiet boy whose only claim to fame seemed to be a second in the 100-metre back-stroke in last July's swimming gala. And his great passion was acknowledged to be butterflies. *'Butterflies?'* Ruth was astonished again.

'Oh, he knows everything about butterflies. And moths.'

At home Ruth said to Ron, 'He knows everything about schooling ponies, too, but how can I get to talk to him?'

'You'll have to get interested in butterflies. And moths,' Ron said.

Ruth made a face. 'That's not one of your very best ideas. I'm just not interested in butterflies. Or moths.'

'I thought it was rather a good idea myself.'

'Yes, well, I should think it is a very interesting subject, if it wasn't that I haven't got time to think about anything else. You see, there's homework now, and it's getting dark earlier. And there aren't any butterflies in the winter anyway.'

'A good point,' said Ron. 'The Pearly Queen's a dead loss,

I take it?'

'Oh, Pearl . . .' Ruth sighed.

Having got involved with Pearl was as much trouble as it was help. Milky Way's presence on rides had certainly got Fly-by-Night steadied down and moving in a less erratic manner, but Ruth now worried more about Milky Way than she did about Fly-by-Night.

'She's such a sweet-natured pony, and the way Pearl treats her is awful. And in spite of being pulled about and jabbed in the mouth and completely muddled, she is so anxious to please all the time. It's that that makes me feel so miserable. If it was Fly, he'd buck Pearl off, or turn round and bite her on the ankle like he does me sometimes, or roll on her or something. He'd stick up for himself. But poor sweet Milky Way just tries all the time, and I get sad.'

'I suppose that's what you pay seven hundred pounds for,' Ron said. 'Not to get rolled on, and your ankles bitten.'

'Oh, yes. She's been most beautifully schooled, and she still remembers it. She always leads on the right leg, and never refuses a jump, and she'll do beautiful forehand turns at gates all off her own bat; but Pearl's no idea. I get ever so miserable, thinking of poor Milky Way.'

'That's daft,' Ron said. 'She'll be well fed, and comfortable most of the time.'

'Yes, I know. She's well fed all right. Stuffed with corn, yet she never gets above herself. But sometimes she goes lame, and Pearl takes no notice.'

'What's wrong with her?'

'I don't know. I told Pearl she ought to get the vet, but she says it's nothing, because it wears off after a bit. Which is true. There's nothing wrong you can see.'

'You've got enough to worry about with your own horse, without worrying about someone else's,' Ron said severely. 'You're a born worrier.'

'Yes. I'm worried about buying hay now. And getting his feet done. Money.'

'Oh, we're all worried about that.'

Ruth knew that her father was worried about it, too. The mortgage on the new house was a large strain on the family finances, and Ruth was frightened to ask for anything for Fly in case her father said he would have to go. She had to manage on her paper-round money. By the end of September the field was so bare that she had to start buying hay, and she soon found that Fly could eat a bale in under a week. When she went up to 'The Place' she would see the gardener, who fed Milky Way, measuring out chaff, oats, bran and pony-nuts, and she longed to be able to do the same. 'Not, of course, that it's necessary,' she told herself. For she knew that Milky Way was grossly overfed for the amount of work she did. But she would have liked a bag of pony-nuts. Half a hundredweight was over a pound to buy. She spent two shillings a week on rough carrots, and scrounged stale toast, and cabbage leaves. When the blacksmith visited 'The Place' to shoe Milky Way, Ruth plucked up her courage and led Fly-by-Night round, and the smith pared his hoofs down for ten shillings.

'Nice l'il feet 'e's got. 'E'll do without shoes if you don't do much with 'im. Just around the fields.'

But Ruth knew he would need shoes when he jumped the Brierley Hill Hunter Trials course. She would have to join the Pony Club, too. She found that this cost a pound. She could not spare a pound, or Fly-by-Night would have starved. 'I'll ask for it for a Christmas present,' she decided. 'Every Christmas.' But if she joined the Pony Club she would have to have jodhpurs, instead of jeans. 'I won't worry about that now,' she said to herself, turning over restlessly in bed. Sometimes when she lay there, watching the deep, wintering sky all rashed over with faint stars, she would hear

Fly-by-Night whinny down the field. The lonely cry would come on the draught through the bedroom window, with the smell of old grass and ploughed earth, and it stabbed Ruth to the heart.

'He's lonely,' she said to herself, eaten with remorse. She could see him, standing in the frosty dark, whinnying to the stars. Sometimes, if she listened hard and the night was still, she would hear Milky Way reply from her open half-door at 'The Place'. 'Lots of people keep just one horse,' Ruth said to herself, trying to be sensible. She always skipped the pages in the pony-books that started, 'The horse is a gregarious animal . . .' It hurt to think that Fly-by-Night was deprived of something essential to his happiness. 'It's daft,' Ron said, 'to worry.' Ruth thought of Ron's sense, and wished she had as much. 'Don't be *sentimental*,' she told herself. She hated sentimentality towards animals, as opposed to sense, but thought that she verged on it herself at times. If she *knew* more, she thought. She would learn at the Pony Club, and meet people who knew, but she could not take Fly-by-Night to the Pony Club until he could be trusted to do as she wanted. She groaned, turning over again in bed so that the eiderdown fell on the floor.

Ruth guessed that Ron had been right when he had said that Pearl was lonely, for Ruth, having introduced herself to Pearl, now found herself badgered by Pearl's company. Unfortunately, with the best will in the world, Ruth could not get fond of Pearl: Pearl exasperated her, with her sulky moods and her bigoted ignorance, which she would not admit. They rode side by side, along the edges of the winter plough, arguing bitterly.

Ruth, compelled by Milky Way's unhappiness, told Pearl she rode on too tight a rein, to which Pearl retorted, 'I ride her collected. I don't let her sprawl about like Fly-by-Night.'

'But a horse should walk on a long rein, freely,' Ruth said. 'You only collect her up when you're going to do something else, to get her ready. Not all the time. You're ruining her mouth.'

'Who are you telling how to ride?' Pearl asked haughtily. 'Just tell me how many times I've fallen off, compared with you?'

'Just staying on doesn't mean to say you are a marvellous rider. Even I could stay on Milky Way. She never gives you any cause to fall off.'

'That's because I'm riding her properly,' Pearl said pointedly. 'If you rode Fly properly he wouldn't buck you off.'

'He doesn't buck,' Ruth said furiously. 'He shies sometimes, that's all. And I've never pretended I can ride well! But at least I'm willing to learn, which is more than you are. Why don't you join the Pony Club? They would teach you.'

'I don't need teaching!' Pearl retorted, equally furiously. 'My pony does what I want her to do, which is more than yours does!'

As if to prove Pearl's point, Fly-by-Night decided at this moment to take exception to a tractor parked beside the hedge some ten feet away. He stopped, goggling, while Milky Way went placidly on. Pearl turned round in her saddle, smirking. Ruth, white with a seething fury, closed her legs firmly, according to the books, but Fly-by-Night started to go backwards. Goaded by Pearl's amusement, Ruth lifted her stick and gave Fly a belt across the quarters with all the strength of her arm. The pony gave an astonished snort, gathered himself abruptly together and shot off like a cork out of a champagne bottle. By clutching a handful of mane, Ruth managed to keep her seat. She had a glimpse of Pearl's laughter and Milky Way's polite curvetting, and then nothing but the stubble racing under the flying hoofs, and the thick mane flying before her. Her eyes were blinded with tears of humiliation, which she pretended were caused by the wind. She did not attempt to pull Fly up, because the field was big, and she did not want to go back to Milky Way. She sat still in the saddle, still holding the mane, until the pony had topped the long rise and Ruth could see the grey water of the tidal creek lying below behind the sea-wall, and the cold pastures stretching away on either side of the river. Then Fly-by-Night dropped his head at last, and fell back into a fast, unbalanced trot, and Ruth was able to pull him up by the gate at the top. She turned round, and to her relief saw that Pearl had cantered round in a big circle and was on her way home, alone. The white Arab pony moved like a drifting sea-gull over the grass, easy, obedient. Ruth watched her, bitter at the injustice of it, while Fly-by-Night hungrily cropped at the tops of the sour yellow thistles that grew in the hedge.

When Pearl had vanished, Ruth, ashamed now of her anger, pulled Fly-by-Night's head up and walked back down the field. He went easily, unconcerned, and Ruth could sit and look at the hedges full of wild rose hips and pretend that she was out to enjoy the landscape. At the bottom of the field, where it was flat, she decided to do some schooling, and walked Fly-by-Night round in several big circles. Apart from a tendency to go out in the bottom corner, heading for home, he did these quite well, but when she attempted to do them at a trot he ran out each time at the home corner, and it was only by a lot of hauling and kicking that she was able to get him back on course again. It was her own inadequacy as much as the pony's that distressed her: into her mind sprang a picture of Peter McNair trotting Fly-by-Night in compass-drawn circles, the pony flexed to the bit, his hind legs well under him. The picture had 'GOOD' written under it. The fact that it was entirely imaginary caused her to weep a little more as she walked

said, 'I've got a new pair of jodhpurs. Do you want my old ones? I was going to throw them away.'

The jodhpurs were beautiful, with buckskin inside the knees, and Ruth found that riding was infinitely more comfortable. She was full of gratitude, and Pearl asked her to tea once or twice, but Ruth never enjoyed life inside 'The Place' very much, for Pearl's parents were very peculiar, to her eyes, using sanguinary adjectives every time they spoke and quite often shouting at each other with a viciousness that made Ruth wish she could crawl under the carpet. At other times they were very affable and called everyone 'darling'. Their house was furnished with very plushy carpets and satin sofas that engulfed one like great soft clouds. Ruth could never make up her mind whether she liked it or not. Its air of lush comfort overwhelmed her, but a puritan streak in her was repelled by it. On the other hand, she did not like her own house very much, with its cold, functional character. She decided that she must be hard to please, until she remembered Mr. Lacey's place, and its haphazard take-it-or-leave-it air, droopy ceilings, and pear trees looking into the bedroom windows. 'That is how I like my places,' she thought.

Three days before she was due to go back to school she went out to feed Fly-by-Night and found him standing in a corner of the field with his nose stuck in the hedge and his tail clamped hard down on his hind quarters. He did not look up as she approached, which was unusual, for he usually galloped towards her whenever she went near the fence.

'What's the matter, my beautiful?'

Fly-by-Night did not shift. Ruth felt a coldness creep over her. She recognized Fly-by-Night's appearance as that described as 'tucked-up' in all the books; he had little hollows under his hip-bones and looked thin. And as she looked at him she saw that he was shivering. His legs shook, and from his back little spirals of steam rose up in the air.

Her coldness turned to panic. She stood rooted, appalled. 'Fly! What's wrong with you?'

But Fly rolled a miserable eye in her direction and put back his ears. His hind legs started to shake so that all his flanks quivered.

Ruth was alone; her father and Ted were at work, and her mother had taken Elizabeth to the dentist. She was terrified, for this ailing Fly-by-Night was a stranger to her, all his cockiness extinguished. The shaking, and the wisps of steam horrified her. She ran back indoors, and hunted feverishly through her books under the chapters headed 'Ailments of the Horse'. These chapters, never much studied until now, laid out in horrid detail the symptoms of worms, thrush, strangles, colic . . . She turned from one heading to another, and found that nearly every paragraph ended, 'Send for the veterinary surgeon immediately.' They nearly all said, too, 'Lead the horse into a box well filled with fresh straw and cover the loins with a rug, or sack.' Ruth, having no box, no straw, no rug, and no sack, pulled the blanket off her bed and took it outside. She threw it over Fly-by-Night's steaming back, fastened it at the front with her school-house brooch and round his belly with two of Ted's belts buckled together. Then, pulling her bicycle out of the garage, she cycled frantically round to 'The Place' to tell Pearl what had happened.

Pearl said, 'Well, get the vet. That's what they're for. We had one for Milly when she cut her leg on some wire.'

'Who was it?'

'Richards, he was called. He's the best round here.'

Ruth hesitated. Doctors were free, but she did not know whether vets had a version of the National Health Service for the animal world. Never having contributed anything towards it, she rather doubted whether they did. Pearl, as if divining her thoughts, said, 'You don't have to pay when he comes. He sends a bill later.' This decided Ruth.

'Can I use your telephone?'

'Yes.'

A secretary took her message. She gave her name and address and the secretary said, 'Mr. Richards will be over as soon as he can.'

Ruth hurried home, and spent the afternoon watching Fly-by-Night, who did not move, and rushing out into the front every time she saw a car. The eleventh car pulled up outside the gate. Ruth looked at it, and started shivering herself. The car was brand-new, with wire wheels, the sort Ted and Ron would watch with narrowed eyes, not saying anything. A man got out and said, 'Horse here?'

Ruth nodded. The man was immaculately dressed in a tweed suit and smelt of after-shave lotion. He took a pair of gum boots out of the car and Ruth said nervously, 'He—he's round the back.'

'Lead on,' said Mr. Richards.

Ruth did as she was told, and took Mr. Richards to Fly-by-Night, who laid back his ears and presented his hind quarters, so that Ruth had to hurry back to the house and fetch a halter. Mr. Richards stood waiting, and Ruth had a terrible feeling that he was like a taxi, his fee creeping up while she wasted his time. But when she haltered Fly-by-Night, Mr. Richards just said, 'These ponies are tough, you know,' and after a cursory thumping, listening and peering he laughed and said, 'What's your mother going to say about the blanket?'

Ruth thought the question completely beside the point.

'Is he all right?'

'Of course he's all right.'

'I—I thought—'

'Oh, you women are all the same. Fuss, fuss, fuss,' said Mr. Richards. 'A little cold. He won't die.'

Ruth felt as if she had been run over by a steam-roller. Mr. Richards drove away and she went back to Fly-by-Night, and cried, 'How was I to know? And he'll send a bill . . .' Fly-by-Night shivered, and Ruth hugged him. 'Oh, Fly, the money!'

The next day Fly-by-Night was better, but Ruth could think of nothing but the little brown bill that would come through the letter-box one morning, addressed, as likely as not, to her father. Her mother was furious about the blanket. When Ruth told Pearl, she just laughed.

7 Peter Takes a Fall

By the time the Pony Club Trials at Brierley came round
again Fly-by-Night, in Ruth's opinion, was not even fit to
take to a Pony Club rally, let alone jump in a Hunter Trials.
Ruth longed for the summer, for long evenings, for more
riding and—most of all—for more grass. The brown bill
from Mr. Richards did not come, but Ruth looked for
it every day. Try as she might, she had managed to save

no more than five shillings towards paying it, but she thought if she could wait until the grass came through, so that there was no more hay to buy, she would be able to save more. 'Worry, worry, worry,' Ron said. But he did not know about Mr. Richards. Nobody knew except Pearl.

And at school Peter McNair was still an unattainable presence, a quiet boy, lately absent quite a lot. Ruth studied him in assembly, but could see no signs of ill health apart from, once, a black eye. Ruth put the black eye down to Woodlark, but had no way of knowing. She had given up any hope now of ever receiving any advice from Peter McNair, or even of speaking to him, and when she went to the Brierley Hunter Trials she expected—correctly, as it turned out—that he would see her without betraying any sign of recognition.

Ruth went to the Brierley Hunter Trials determined that next year she would ride in it. And it was a sign of her progress to remember that last year, standing on the same ground, she did not even possess a pony, or even dare to hope that she ever might. However unsatisfactory she might consider her schooling of Fly-by-Night, at least she now had a potential entry. 'It's just up to me,' she said to herself, which was in no way a comfort. But she went to Brierley this time, knowing what she wanted. 'Just to get round, next year.' Not even to win.

It was warmer, this year, the air full of the smell of spring. The little wood was full of catkins, and the stream was swollen, the banks soft and peaty. Ruth walked the course, while the stewards were still pushing in the marker flags and the riders were converging at the gate at the top of the hill. The course was basically the same as the year before, but with variations. This year one jumped the course through the wood in the opposite direction, so that one jumped into it over a rail and down the steep bank, and left it by passing through the gate. Having considered all the difficulties, Ruth went back to the collecting-ring to wait for the start. She felt tight and nervous, thinking of next year. 'Whatever shall I feel like next year?' she wondered, and started to shiver.

The girls' faces this year were familiar. The girl whom Peter McNair had asked to pair with him was there, and the girl on the lazy grey who had objected to the idea. All the ponies looked competent and unworried; the girls sat and talked as if they were quite unconcerned. The ponies did not kick and go round in circles, nor even try to graze. They just stood. 'If Fly just stood,' Ruth thought enviously. It had never occurred to her before that it was something a pony had to learn.

This year Peter McNair arrived in a modest single trailer driven by his father. The pony they unloaded from it was a bay mare of about fourteen hands, more like a show-pony than a hunter. She had a fine thoroughbred head with a white star, and an airy, floating movement that reminded Ruth of Milky Way. She would not have known who it was if she had not bought a programme, and seen the name Woodlark.

'Woodlark!' Ruth stared. She remembered vividly the wildness of the bay filly, galloping along the crest of the big field; she had not dreamed that even the McNairs could have tamed such a creature so quickly. The day after she had seen Woodlark she had bought Fly-by-Night. 'They have had exactly the same time as I have had,' she thought. And Fly-by-Night would not even trot in a circle!

She would have been acutely depressed if Peter McNair had mounted and ridden away to sit unconcernedly in the collecting-ring. But her spirits lifted a little when she saw that the McNair magic was not so potent as she had supposed. Peter, in fact, looked unhappy, and seemed to be having a bitter argument with his father. Mr. McNair stood at the mare's head while Peter saddled her, and his hands were full keeping her still: it was obvious that she was far from composed.

Ruth heard McNair say, 'Of course she'll go round. I haven't brought her all this way just for the drive.' His voice was very curt, the sort one would not wish to argue with, and Peter said no more. His head was under the saddle flap as he did up the girths and Ruth could not see his expression. She was fascinated, eavesdropping from a discreet distance.

When the mare was saddled, Peter mounted. He sat very still in the saddle, not saying anything, his face closed up and showing nothing. His father led the mare for a few paces and then let go, and Peter kept her walking, away from the crowd and the horse-boxes. Ruth thought, 'From the way the mare goes, it must feel like sitting on a volcano.' She thought, too, that Woodlark was one pony that would not stand still in the collecting-ring. Peter made no attempt to bring her near any of the other ponies, but kept her out of the way, walking and trotting.

'Perhaps she's not so different from Fly after all,' Ruth reflected. 'Except that she's got Peter, and Fly's only got me.'

She had not attempted to jump Fly-by-Night yet, except over poles on the ground and small ditches, which did not trouble him. Some of the jumps on the trial course looked quite big to her eyes, although very clean and inviting. She thought the nastiest was the jump over the rail and down into the wood, and decided to stand there, in the same place as last year, so that she could see most of the course. A man sat on a camp-stool in the wood, with a score-sheet on his lap. Ruth stood by the hedge and waited for the first pony to come, glad of the warm sun.

Some of the ponies did fast competent rounds, but many

of them were not at all marvellous, and Ruth, as is the way with competitors, felt very cheered. This course was a thing between oneself and one's pony: half the time one was alone, out in the country, and there were no spectators apart from one's fellow competitors, who knew what it felt like, and the adults scoring on their camp-stools. 'I *shall* get round,' Ruth said to herself. 'Oh, I shall do it!'

Woodlark jumped last in the class for twelve- to fourteen-year-olds, having been kept out of the collecting-ring until it was nearly empty. Ruth recognized her by her gallop: she went up the hill as if on wings, twice as fast as any of the other competitors. Whether Peter had her under control or not Ruth could not tell, until she appeared on the far side of the wood, still galloping, and Ruth assumed she must have cleared the intervening obstacles. Peter was just sitting there, not pulling at her nor seeming—from a distance—in any way alarmed; in fact, as they flew a fence out in the country it looked to Ruth so easy that for a moment she wondered why she was so worried about trying it herself. And why Peter himself had seemed unhappy about the idea. But as the mare circled for home and came at her floating gallop across the field to what Ruth thought of as 'her' jump, Ruth began to change her mind.

The jump into the wood was cramped between trees and the bank down to the stream was poached and steep. Most ponies had slithered down it on their hocks, or gone down in surprised and unseating bounds. It was not an obstacle to take fast, and Peter was pulling Woodlark up in plenty of time. As she came nearer, Ruth could see that, although Peter had her collected, she looked very wild, and anything but an easy ride. Peter was watching the dark hole into the wood, frowning, and Woodlark, held back, was taking great bounds up into the air like a Lipizzaner stallion. Peter eased his hands. The mare plunged forward, fast, and galloped at the rail, but at the last moment she decided she didn't like the look of it, and stopped.

Unfortunately she had left it a fraction too late. Skidding in the mud, she cannoned into the rail and pitched right over it in a spectacular cartwheel. Ruth saw her shoulders drop, her tail fly up in the air. There was the splattering of mud clods and a crashing of branches, then some anguished snorts, a cry of anger, or pain, and a lot more splashing. Ruth ran forward, more by instinct than inclination, but as she got to the splintered rail Woodlark came bounding back up the bank, wild-eyed. She hesitated at the top, quivering, too frightened to jump out, and too frightened to go back. Her reins were over her neck and trailing between her forelegs.

Ruth knew she ought to try to catch her, and tried a soothing address, but her voice came out anything but soothing. Woodlark, churning about, saw her, swung away —but the man taking scores was coming up the bank behind her. Woodlark, cornered, swung round again and jumped, clean and high.

'Catch her!' the man bawled at Ruth.

Ruth made a rugby tackle at Woodlark's head, and caught a handful of mane. She gripped tight and Woodlark pulled her off her balance. She cried out as Woodlark trod hard on her foot, groped up with her other hand for something better than mane, and fell over as the mare stumbled, treading on her reins. Fortunately, as Ruth fell she caught the vital rein, and held on tight. Woodlark started off with a great bound, but was brought up abruptly. Ruth felt herself dragged across the grass, but somehow managed to get to her feet again, winded and unable to utter a word, soothing or otherwise. But at this moment the man caught up with her and Ruth saw his hairy tweed arm reach over beside her own. Woodlark was captured. Ruth let go, shaken.

'Well done, my dear,' said the man. 'It was misguided of me to shout "Catch her", but I know this mare. We wouldn't have got our hands on her for a fortnight if once she'd got away.'

Ruth nodded, still panting. Even the large man had his hands full holding Woodlark. She turned round to see what had happened to Peter, and saw him emerging from the wood, climbing the rail. Ruth expected him to look shocked and pale, but, apart from the fact that he was covered in mud, he looked as if nothing untoward had happened at all.

'Is she all right?' he asked.

'Seems to be,' the man said.

There seemed to be no question of Peter's not continuing, in spite of the severity of the fall. After a brief examination of the mare's forelegs, he went round to the near-side to mount, while the man endeavoured to hold her. Woodlark was in a frenzy of nervous excitement, swinging round in circles, her hind legs bunched beneath her. Peter stood patiently, waiting his moment, then was up and in the saddle with one movement so that the mare scarcely knew it.

The man grinned and said, 'Your father selling this as a child's first pony?'

'More like tenth, I should think,' Peter said.

'Wait till I get back to my seat.'

The man let go and hurried away, and Peter turned the mare away and cantered her in a tight circle. Ruth went back to her spot in the hedge, not envying Peter at all. He went to the bar slowly, holding the mare in, so that she was almost cantering on the spot. Peter's face showed nothing but intense concentration. Ruth held her breath for him, more nervous than he. She could see the wildness in the mare's eyes, and the curbed energy in her pirouetting hind legs. With a lesser rider she would have run out, or stopped, but, by what seemed a miracle to Ruth, Peter got her clear over the bar and down the bank in impeccable style. He rode her through the wood, twisting and turning through the trees, but when she saw the way out through the gate, and the open field beyond, she fought for her bit, pulling like a train. Peter managed to stop her, but then could not get her to approach the gate at all. Thwarted in her desire to do as she wished, Woodlark started to go up on her hind legs.

Ruth groaned to herself, watching the exhibition with a sweaty feeling, as if she were personally involved. 'Suppose Fly-by-Night does this next year?' she thought. But immediately she knew that Fly-by-Night was no Woodlark, exasperating as she might find him at times. Peter was on his own with Woodlark, fighting a personal battle, for Ruth could see that the stewards up the hill were getting ready for the next class, having given up waiting for the reappearance of the little mare out of the wood. The scoring man was waiting, but impatiently, knowing that his score-sheet was wanted up the field. Presently the girl Ruth called Cat's Eyes came cantering down the field on the grey pony to collect it, and the man climbed up the muddy bank to hand it over.

'Major Banks says please will you clear the course,' she said.

The man turned round and bawled through the wood, 'Will you retire, please, Peter!'

As Peter had been trying to get out of the wood for the last five minutes, Ruth did not see that the instruction was going to alter anything for him. Woodlark, covered with sweat, was still napping sulkily, but with less vigour, and was appreciably nearer to the gate. Given time, Peter was going to win, but his orders to retire altered the situation. Ruth, watching, and thinking, 'Whatever will he do?' did not guess that the problem could be so easily resolved. Peter turned Woodlark away from the gate and cantered her back some forty feet along the path. Then, turning her sharply on her hocks, he sent her off at a sharp pace towards the gate. She flew the obstacle with at least two feet to spare and galloped away back to the collecting-ring.

Ruth went back up the hill, tired, as if she had confronted all Peter's problems herself. Every time she thought of herself doing it all on Fly-by-Night she went hot and cold with fright. 'If I feel like this now,' she thought, 'what will I feel like on the actual day?' It was a daunting thought, to be countered with scornful, Ron-like opinions to put the whole thing in its proper place: a potty Pony Club competition without even any spectators . . . as if it mattered whether one fell in a ditch or won a red rosette. It was a nothing . . . fun for the kiddies . . .

Obviously Mr. McNair did not think it a nothing. When Ruth got to the top of the hill she saw that Woodlark was already unsaddled and ready to go into the trailer. Mr. McNair stood by her with a sharp look in his eyes, smoking a cigarette and not looking at all sympathetic. He was talking to Peter and, although Ruth could not hear what he was saying, she could tell that it was nasty. She watched from a distance, pricking with indignation. McNair ought to be glad that Peter was alive, after a fall like that, she thought. But Peter, coming out of the horse-box, did not seem to be upset. His face, as usual, showed no expression, but Ruth thought that, if he had any feelings at all, he must be fed up.

She hoped, after catching Woodlark in that spectacular fashion, Peter might remember her face and acknowledge her the next time they passed at school. But when school started again, Peter, in blazer and flannels, was as remote as he had ever been.

It was spring, and the grass was growing; the sun had warmth again. Ruth decided to start learning about butterflies.

8 'In Need of Care and Protection'

Ron, the ever-helpful, said he had a good book on butter-flies which he would lend her. Ruth did not think the idea was likely to bear fruit, and could not help getting the giggles when the boys inquired politely how the lepidoptery was going.

One spring evening, when Ruth was leaning on the kitchen window-sill, thinking how nicely the grass was growing, the familiar racket of the motor bike came to a crescendo in the drive outside, shutting out the noise of next door's lawn-mower. Mrs. Hollis automatically went to the oven to get Ted's dinner out, but when the door opened it was Ron who stood there, not Ted.

'Oh, Mrs. Hollis,' he said in a queer voice.

Ruth looked up sharply. Ron was as white as a sheet.

'What is it?' her mother said.

'It's Ted. He—he's—'

'He's had an accident?'

Ruth felt herself go cold all over. Her mother stood by the oven, tense, bright-eyed.

Ron nodded.

'How bad is it?' How sharp, how cool her mother was, Ruth thought, amazed. Just as if she had expected it all the time. It was Ron who looked terrible. Ruth was shivering.

'He's not—not dead. I don't know how bad. They've taken him to Burnt Wood casualty.'

'Sit down,' Mrs. Hollis said to Ron. 'Here.' She pulled a chair out for him, and took his crash-helmet. 'The kettle's boiling. I'll make you a cup of tea, and some brandy in it.' She sounded completely matter-of-fact, as if Ron had come to tell her that Ted would be late for tea. Ron buried his face in his hands and said, 'I didn't know it could happen like that, so quick. Oh God, it was awful.' He was almost crying.

Mrs. Hollis was very gentle with Ron, as if what had happened to Ted was of no importance. Ruth, enormously impressed by her mother's self-control, could not stop crying. Nothing like this had ever touched her before: the evening remained fixed in her memory ever afterwards as the blackest thing that had ever happened. When her father came home he took her mother to the hospital, where she stayed all night and the next day as well. The hours passed like days. Ted was critically ill with concussion and several fractures. Ruth, like Ron, could not believe that the irrepressible Ted could possibly be extinguished so simply, in spite of the fact that the newspapers were full of tales of fatal accidents every day; she prayed stubbornly, as up till now she had only prayed for Fly-by-Night, and every morning woke to the feeling that she came to think of as 'a dark cloud'. The house seemed quite different without Ted in it.

Ruth thought that if Ted merely went on living her dark cloud would dissolve and life would, by comparison, become rosy and sweet once more. But life, of course—she realized rather bitterly a few weeks later—is not so simple. Ted was pronounced out of danger, but the consequences of the accident now spread a different sort of gloom through the house.

Ruth, washing up in the kitchen, heard her father say to her mother over his cup of tea, 'It's only when a thing like this happens that it comes home to me how much we've been counting on Ted's money. It was all wrong, of course, but knowing his tenner a week was there was always a nice thought. It's been nothing but worry since we saddled ourselves with this mortgage.'

Ruth heard her mother say something about going out to work and her father replied. 'That would mean giving up Elizabeth.' There were a few more sentences she did not catch, and then she heard her father say, half-humorously, 'Poor Ruthie will be selling papers to feed herself, let alone that darned pony of hers.'

'You'd like to give up this house, wouldn't you?'

'I'd like to stop having to worry about money.'

Ruth went on washing up, with a cold feel in the pit of

her stomach. Fly-by-Night was so vulnerable, when her parents talked about money. Keeping him on the paper money was desperately hard as it was, and was going to be a lot harder when she started getting him shod. And next year he would need to be in hard condition for the Hunter Trials, which would mean more expensive food—not to mention the Pony Club subscription. Ruth knew that if she started thinking about all this, she would feel sick. It had happened before.

Later on, before she went to bed, her father said to her, quite gently, 'Ruth, this pony of yours . . .'

'I pay for him all myself,' Ruth said frantically. 'I've never asked you for anything, not since the saddle!'

Her father put down a little brown envelope on the table. It was addressed to him. Inside was a bill for three pounds, thirteen shillings and sixpence.

'But he never even did anything!' Ruth wept, incensed by the tactlessness of Mr. Richards's timing in sending out his bill, as much as by the bill itself. 'He only said I fussed!'

'He came,' her father said sadly. 'That's what they charge for, just coming. You don't make a habit of this?' he added, waving the bill.

'Only once. And I shall pay it. It's not for you. It's mine. He addressed it wrong.'

'I shall pay it,' her father said firmly.

'But you—'

'Look, things may be difficult, but I'm not so hard up that I can't pay this bill. Now stop crying. I'm not angry. But if this happens another time, I want you to tell me, not keep it secret.'

'Yes.'

Thank heaven, Ruth thought, that summer had come, and the field was bright with new grass. There was no more hay to buy, and she could save her money, get a hoard in for next winter. She wondered, now, if she was desperately selfish, to want this thing so badly? With all the family troubles?

'But what difference would it make if you gave him up?' Ron said very sensibly. 'It wouldn't pay off the mortgage, what you would get for him.'

'No one would buy him, the way he is,' Ruth said.

'Things'll come all right,' Ron said optimistically. 'They usually do. Ted's coming along fine.'

That was the main thing, after all, Ruth remembered. Ted was going to be in hospital for three months, the doctors said. Ron and Ruth went to visit him on the nights her parents didn't go (on the motor bike, but slowly, in deference to Mrs. Hollis's instruction). He had been put on to basket-making, to while away the time, and had been carried away with creative fervour, weaving baskets five feet high.

'What are they *for*?' Ruth asked, amazed.

'Waste-paper baskets,' Ted said happily.

'But nobody's got that much waste paper,' said Ron.

One evening, when Ruth was waiting for Ron to pick her up, a woman arrived at the door. Ruth, answering the bell, recognized her as Mrs. Challoner, the Child Care woman, and asked her in.

'I hope you don't mind my calling at this time,' the woman said to Ruth's mother, 'but something urgent has come up, and I've come to see if you can help me out. It's only a short-term case, a child we think would be better away from its parents for a month or so. Needs a stable atmosphere, just to be accepted into a normal family, carry on at school, no fuss. The psychiatrist passed it on to me, and I wondered if you could possibly help.'

Ron called at this moment, and Ruth left her parents discussing the situation with the woman in the living-room, and went out into the kitchen with Ron. She repeated what she had heard to Ron, and Ron said, 'It'll get a stable atmosphere here all right, if you've got anything to do with it.'

Ruth smiled. 'Of course, Ted's room's empty now, so I expect Mum will agree.'

They went to the hospital and told Ted that his bed was being taken over. 'You'll be out in the garage when you come home,' Ron told him. 'Better start weaving yourself a bed.'

'They're out of cane,' Ted said sadly. 'The old girl says I've used up six months' stock. I've sounded her out about having the cylinder head in here so that I can polish the parts—but she wasn't very keen. She's starting me on tapestry tomorrow.'

'Very nice, my boy, very nice. Knitting's next on the list, after tapestry. And when you've used up six months' stock of wool there are a few bales of crochet cotton down in the storeroom.'

When Ruth got home she found her parents watching television.

'Are we having that child?' she asked curiously.

Her mother nodded. 'Yes. It's only for a month or two. Mrs. Challoner is bringing me all the details tomorrow morning, and says she'll deliver the child in the afternoon. How's Ted, by the way?'

'He's doing tapestry.'

This evoked some amusement, and Mrs. Hollis said she would take him socks to darn the following evening. 'You see that this new child has a pleasant evening tomorrow, Ruth. It's a pity we've got to go out the first night, but the sister wants to speak to us. I told Mrs. Challoner how we're fixed, but she seems to think it will work out all right. So we'll give it a trial.'

Ruth went home from school the following evening,

curious, and a little nervous. It was a warm evening. The children were playing in the road with tricycles and skipping-ropes, and soon the open-plan fronts would whirr to the noise of lawn-mowers. She thought of Ted, imprisoned in his bed for the sake of a moment's over-impetuosity on the motor bike, and was sorry for him. 'He should have done it in November, if he was going to do it at all,' she thought.

She went in through the kitchen door.

'Oh, Ruth,' her mother said. There was a boy sitting at the table, reading a newspaper. 'This is Peter, Ruth, who's going to stay for a bit.'

It was Peter McNair.

9 Ruth Watches Television

Ruth was so shattered by the unexpectedness of the situation that she could not speak. She opened her mouth, and no words came out. Peter looked up and said, 'Oh hullo,' without much interest, and Mrs. Hollis said, 'I suppose you two know each other, if you're at the same school? By sight, at any rate.'

'Yes,' Peter said.

Ruth shut her mouth, as it would not work, and dropped her satchel on the floor.

Mrs. Hollis said to Peter, 'Do you like liver and bacon?' and Peter replied, 'Yes, I don't mind it.'

'Pick up your satchel, Ruth,' Mrs. Hollis said. 'Are you sickening for something? You look blotchy.'

'No,' Ruth said dimly. She groped for her satchel, and fled out of the kitchen. She ran upstairs, and locked herself in the lavatory. She was shaking all over, and felt an insane desire to laugh out loud. In her satchel she had a book on butterflies. 'But he's downstairs! Here to stay! *Him!* Of all the people in the world . . .'

'Ruth, are you being sick or something?' her mother asked outside the door.

'No, I'm all right.'

'Well, before you come down, just make up Ted's bed, will you? I don't seem to have got anything done today, and the dinner's cooking now. I've put the sheets out.'

Ruth did as she was told. Ted's room was impersonal without Ted's untidiness stamping it. Ruth spread the sheets and felt herself coming back to earth, warm, elated. The shock dissolved into a feeling of utter satisfaction at the ways of the world. By the time she was smoothing the quilt the satisfaction had given way to a feeling of extreme curiosity as to why Peter McNair had come into the Child Care Department, and why he was better parted from his parents. As far as she knew, he did not have a mother. But from what she had last seen of his father it did not seem unreasonable to suppose that Peter would be happier away from him. Who had interceded for him? she wondered. She had noticed that he had been away from school for the last three days, but it had never entered her wildest dreams that he could be the urgent case Mrs. Challoner had been talking about.

She went downstairs slowly, back into the kitchen. Elizabeth was laying the table with a lot of clatter; the bacon was spluttering noisily under the grill, and Peter stood staring out of the window with his hands in his pockets. Fly-by-Night was out of sight in the field, but Peter showed no interest in the hoof-marked back garden. Always a reserved boy, it occurred to Ruth that, during the time she had known him, he had got gradually more and more withdrawn. Because he rarely showed any emotions, it did not mean, she realized, that he did not feel any, and what was happening to him now could scarcely be less than a personal crisis in his life; yet he did not look upset. He had the slightly watchful expression in his eyes that Ruth now knew was his normal expression; his whole attitude was one of observing, recording, and passing no opinion. But Ruth saw now that it was not because he had no opinions to pass. For the first time it occurred to her that, under his stocky, unrevealing shell, he was very much aware, and as sensitive to hurt as any more normally extroverted child, if not more so. And really, when it came to the subject of problems to solve, he had more troubles by far than she had. It was more to the point now that she should try to make things come right for Peter than that he should make things come right for her. This change of outlook came to Ruth in the moment that it took her mother to pull the grill-pan out from under the grill, and say, 'Ruth, make the tea.'

'Elizabeth, wash your hands. They're filthy,' Ruth said, from force of habit, going to the tea-caddy. How strangely things worked out, she was thinking. Her mother put out the meal for the three of them, and they sat down to it. Peter had a good appetite, whatever his spiritual starvation, and there was no need to force a conversation when they were all so healthily occupied. When he had finished Peter said to Mrs. Hollis, 'Can I go and have a look round before it gets dark? Isn't there a creek at the bottom of the lane—the lane that goes to the right, off the estate?'

'Yes, there is,' Ruth said.

'You can go,' Mrs. Hollis said. 'But be back by seven, before I have to go out.'

'Can I come?' Elizabeth asked Peter.

'I don't mind,' Peter said.

Elizabeth leapt eagerly from the table and fetched her gum boots. Peter went out with her, apparently quite happy that she should accompany him.

'I'm glad she wanted to go,' Mrs. Hollis said to Ruth, pouring herself a cup of tea and sitting down rather wearily. 'She'll keep tabs on him. He's not likely to throw himself in, with her around. And I didn't want to say no to him, the first night.'

Ruth looked at her mother, shocked. 'Throw himself in? Surely it's not that bad?'

'Well, no normal, happy child presents itself at a police-station and says it refuses to go home, and please could they find it somewhere to live. Which is apparently what he did.'

'But very sensible, if you feel like that,' Ruth couldn't help pointing out. 'Better than running away in an aimless fashion. And his father is beastly.'

'So I understand. Mrs. Challoner had to do some investigating, and went to see him, and said that he was absolutely flabbergasted at what Peter had done. He said if he came back it would all be all right, but Peter flatly refused to go. It seems that since the mother died, three or four years ago, the father more or less drowned his sorrows in work, to the exclusion of all else.'

'The horse-dealing business,' Ruth put in.

'Yes. I realized it was the same McNairs that you went to see last year, when Mrs. Challoner was telling me all this. Apparently Peter was expected to go along with his father, and submerge himself in the horse business, too, but Peter had other ideas. It seems he's not the slightest bit interested in horses. He didn't worry very much at first, but as he got older, and presumably more competent, his father expected him to be riding all the time. He started keeping him away from school, just to ride. And Peter got fed up. The last straw was apparently when his father stopped him eating bread and potatoes because he was getting too heavy. So he just walked out.'

'Good for him.'

'Mrs. Challoner thought it would just be a matter of talking Peter into going back home, and smoothing things over, but when the psychiatrist fellow looked into it, he said Peter was on no account to go back. So that's how we got landed with him. Mrs. Challoner knew about Ted, so knew we had a spare room. And round she came.'

'Queer,' Ruth said. She was still bemused by the way things had worked out. 'He's a marvellous rider.'

Her mother looked at her sharply. 'After what I've told you, I hope you'll have more sense than to start talking horses to him. I told Mrs. Challoner that she might not have chosen a very good place for him, what with you and your horse-nonsense, but she didn't think that merely seeing a pony out of his bedroom window would be more than he could bear. But you're on no account to trouble him with your pony problems, Ruth.'

'No, I won't.'

'That's the one thing that really wouldn't do him any good at all. He has to go and see the psychiatrist once a week, so they must consider he needs watching. I don't want you to upset him.'

'No, I wouldn't!' Ruth said indignantly.

'We've enough problems to get on with at the moment. We don't want any more.' Mrs. Hollis finished her cup of tea and looked at the time. 'Your father will be in in a minute. I must put his meal on.'

Ruth started to do her homework on the cleared end of the table. But she could not concentrate on what she was supposed to be doing. She kept thinking of Peter being under her nose all the time, and herself not being able to ask him about Fly-by-Night, when everything went wrong.

'Torture,' she thought, digging her pencil deep into her notebook, making an agonized doodle. 'Cruelty to children.' She drew a little girl, transfixed by an arrow. 'It's me that will be going to the psychiatrist when Peter's finished.' She longed to tell Ron what had happened, and see the expression on his face.

All her tack was dirty and needed cleaning, but she spent the evening watching the television. Peter sat on the other end of the sofa, staring at the screen. The only conversation that passed between them at all was a few desultory remarks about school.

10 Pearl Makes a Bet

It was a hot summer, the hottest for years. The ground was baked hard, and big cracks opened up in the clay down by the creek. Ruth rode Fly-by-Night along the dry paths, her thighs sticky with heat against the saddle, flies singing in a cloud round the pony's head. If it hadn't been for the goal she was working for, she would have been very content. Fly-by-Night had stopped bolting with her; he trotted and cantered when she asked, and nearly always stopped when she wanted. But he had a definite mind of his own, which was still a match for her riding. There were days when she had battles with him, long-drawn-out miserable affairs which she won by patience rather than skill. She could not rely on his obedience; she could not be sure, when approaching even a small ditch, that he was going to jump it. The fences at Brierley were as impossible as mountains, by his present standards.

Ron said, 'If you take him to a Pony Club meeting, they will teach you how to do it. Isn't that what it's for?'

Ruth agreed that it was. 'They only meet in the school holidays. I'll go to the first one in August.' She did not want to admit to Ron that the thought of going to the first meeting terrified her. She was afraid Fly-by-Night would make a fool of her in front of all those competent girls.

Even if she had not been given definite instructions about not troubling Peter with her 'nonsense', Ruth realized, as she got to know Peter better, that her own instinct would have stopped her from opening the subject. It was as if Peter, normal in all other respects, had put up a sort of barrier where horses were concerned. He never passed a comment on Fly-by-Night, seeming almost not to see him. When Ruth passed him out riding—which she did quite often, for he went down to the creek a lot to swim, or look for butterflies—he would just nod his head to her, but never linger, or stop to watch, or pass any remark. He never mentioned any of his riding experiences, or his home, or his father, or his brothers, as if none of his past life had ever happened. Ruth supposed this was a symptom of the disturbance that the psychiatrist was interested in, but when she asked him what he did at the psychiatrist's—having pictured him lying on a couch recounting his life-history— he said, 'Oh, we go to Lyons and eat chocolate éclairs,' which did not help Ruth at all.

But in all other respects Peter became a normal member of the family. He was no trouble at all, quiet, obedient, perfectly good-natured. At first he hardly spoke at all, but gradually he thawed out. He smiled more often, and at school, Ruth noticed, was far more lively than he had been.

When the time came for Ted to come home from hospital Mr. and Mrs. Hollis decided that he might just as well stay. They had got used to having him around, and there was room for another bed in Ted's room. Mrs. Challoner was very pleased with their decision. 'He's settled down so well with you. It would be such a shame to have to move him just at the moment. His father's gone abroad, you know, so perhaps the change will do the gentleman good. I hope so, because Peter will have to go back to him eventually.' Ruth hoped the nasty Mr. McNair would stay abroad for a long time. She liked Peter, and was still hopeful that, after a few more sessions eating chocolate éclairs, he would get round to talking 'horse-nonsense' with her.

As the first meeting of the Pony Club approached at the end of July she tried to convince herself that she had nothing to worry about, but she was not very successful. She tried to tell herself that this meeting would, in fact, solve her problems, because that's what the meetings were for, but she dreaded her introduction to the ranks of those capable, cold-eyed girls. She longed to ask Peter about them, and about what happened at the meetings. She got as far as saying to him, 'I'm going to a Pony Club meeting on Wednesday,' but Peter only said, 'And the best of British luck,' which did nothing to make her feel any more optimistic. If he thought she needed it, it was no more than she felt herself.

Having prevailed upon Pearl—in vain—to join the Pony Club and accompany her, Ruth resigned herself to the awfulness of this first experience, and spent most of Tuesday on a marathon cleaning operation, of her pony, her tack, and her shabby clothes. As the day went on she got gloomier and gloomier, so that in the evening Ted and Ron kept passing remarks about the joy of owning the most faithful of man's servants, a horse.

'If I were you, I'd take up basket-weaving instead,' Ted

told her. 'You could get a fair old load of cane for the cost of that brute.'

But the brute, when she had finished, did look lovely. Ruth was cheered when she went out again in the evening, and saw him grazing under the trees in the last of the sun, the golden light adding an extra burnish to the work she had put in on his coat during the afternoon. He had filled out beautifully since the spring, yet was not too fat, for Ruth had been keeping him in the garden all day, where the grass was very spare, and only letting him into the builder's field at night. And his extra inches were muscle, not flabby fat; his shoulders and quarters were hard and strong, his eyes bright with good health. When he saw her at the fence he came cantering up, as he always did now, and pushed his nose at her eagerly. She rarely gave him titbits, for he had taken to biting when she had given him too many. Now, at least, he never bit, but he still gobbled his lips at her in his thrusting pony way, all bounce and push. Fly had never been a pony to just stand and let himself be stroked.

'Be good tomorrow, please,' Ruth whispered, and sent up a little prayer to the first star.

Having ridden very little on roads, Ruth had worked out a route to the meeting mostly through lanes, and when she had to go where there was traffic she got off and led Fly-by-Night. She supposed this was all wrong, but she did not want to be landed under a car for the sake of principle. As he was not shod, she had always put off taking him on roads, but now she realized that it was a part of his education that she would not be able to put off much longer.

Fortunately for her pride, she was mounted and progressing quite satisfactorily when four girls on ponies clattered out of a turning just ahead of her. She felt Fly-by-Night gather himself together underneath her; she sat down tight and took a firm hold on the reins, and was just able to prevent

102

him in his mad rush forward from cannoning into the hind quarters of the last pony. The rider turned round and gave Ruth a surprised look, as Fly-by-Night let out an excited whinny. Ruth, crimson, said, 'I'm sorry.' She could feel Fly-by-Night's excitement, the very thing she had dreaded; he was bouncing beneath her, snatching at the bit, swinging his quarters about.

To her great relief the girls ahead of her turned into a field gate, and she found, following them, that she had arrived at her destination. She was committed now. Whatever happened, she felt, was now out of her hands. She could but do her feeble best.

Beneath her, Fly-by-Night, taking in the scene, trembled with excitement. There were about thirty ponies in the field, and a middle-aged, military-looking man with a fierce black moustache—whom Ruth remembered was Major Banks—was bawling at them all to assemble in the middle and circle round him. With him there were two or three older girls, more or less grown-up, and an elderly man sitting on a shooting-stick. She had just arrived in time. Without dismounting, she cast off her shoulder bag with sandwiches and her headcollar in it, so that it landed under a convenient bush, and headed Fly-by-Night hopefully towards the circling riders.

He went like a coiled spring, in bounds of excitement, whinnying loudly. Ruth was preoccupied with keeping him from getting out of control; she knew from the way he fought her hands that at any minute he would get his nose up in the air and rush off headlong. Major Banks was eyeing her nervously, but Ruth's eyes were fixed on Fly-by-Night's amazed ears, flexing backwards and forwards.

'Steady, steady, you little idiot!' she muttered, but her voice was as nervous as Fly's progress.

She managed to join the circle, with Fly dashing and darting, crowding the pony in front, and still letting out his frantic neighs. The girl behind wisely kept her pony at a distance, for which Ruth was greatly relieved, for she was afraid Fly would kick.

Major Banks was picking out the competent riders for the more advanced training, and the ones left circling, Ruth concluded, were the ones for the elementary class. Just as she was thinking that perhaps the worst of Fly-by-Night's astonishment was giving way to acceptance of this strange new game, the competent group was sent away to the other side of the field. As the riders set off at a fast trot, in a big bunch, Fly-by-Night took off in pursuit, whipping round out of the circle and breaking into the wild canter that Ruth had been dreading. She pulled at him, but he put his nose up, snatching at the bit.

Ruth heard Major Banks roar something at her, but she knew she was on her own. She sat down as firmly as she could to the lurching, unbalanced pace, and heaved desperately on the left rein to circle Fly back to where he had come from. With his head pulled round he galloped on as best as he could, but Ruth's brute strength gradually prevailed, and he started to slow up, in big jerks, showing the whites of his eyes.

Ruth, bitterly embarrassed, turned him round towards the group she was supposed to be with, but he refused to go in this direction, and napped round to face the other way. With brute force once more Ruth hauled him round again, and drummed him with her heels. He faced the right way, but would not move, except backwards. By the time Major Banks reached her, Ruth was biting back tears of humiliation.

'What's all this, animal?' Major Banks said quite cheerfully, reaching out a hand to Fly-by-Night's bridle. 'You want to be with the others, do you? Well, we want you over here.'

He put a hand on the reins and led Fly-by-Night, who went without any more trouble. Ruth sat still, sick with despair. The two groups of ponies were now circling with one of the other girls in the centre of each; everyone was occupied, and Major Banks halted Fly-by-Night and looked at Ruth, stroking Fly's neck.

'You didn't manage that too badly,' he said. 'Don't look too worried. Young, is he?'

'Yes, he's four. I had him when he was three.'

'You had him unbroken, I take it?'

'Yes.'

The Major shook his head and tut-tutted. 'Same old story. These so nice but quite crazy parents will buy their children a sweet, wild pony, and expect them to grow up together.' He smiled at Ruth quite pleasantly. 'Hard, isn't it?'

'Yes,' said Ruth stiffly. 'Only I bought him myself. My parents had nothing to do with it.'

'Even worse,' said the Major cheerfully. He stood back, surveying the now resigned Fly-by-Night thoughtfully. 'I'll say this for you, you've an eye for a nice pony. Very nice.'

Ruth's spirits rose a notch.

'We've had wilder animals than this in the Pony Club.'

Ruth's spirits rose another notch.

'Join the others,' said Major Banks. 'He'll be all right.'

Fly-by-Night, having fastened his eyes on the right set of ponies, joined them without any further trouble, walking in a circle round the instructor, a dashing-looking girl of about twenty slashing a crop against her gum boots. Ruth could feel vibrations of amazement still coming up through Fly, but his demeanour was now more subdued. She began to think she might be able to cope.

For an hour and a half they rode in circles, walking and trotting, first all together, then one by one, then in a long row over a very low cavaletti, then one by one. Ruth, concentrating hard, never had time to wonder what the others were thinking of her; they all had their problems, too, she came to realize. And most of them didn't have such a handsome pony as hers. On the other side of the field the more advanced riders were doing much the same thing with Major Banks, only their jumps were bigger and their circles were smaller, and the performances were altogether more polished.

At lunch-time Ruth had hoped to talk to some of the girls and perhaps find the understanding friend she was always hoping for, but Fly-by-Night, tied to the hedge, kept getting his feet tangled up in his headrope because he was still excited, and she had to untie him after a few crises and spend the lunch-hour holding the end of the rope herself. As he kept darting about every few minutes, and she was trying to eat sandwiches at the same time, it was not at all restful. She was very envious of the girls whose ponies stood dozing, and who were able to picnic on rugs with bottles of pop and no troubles. She realized that there were things Fly-by-Night had to learn that she had not even thought of yet.

When it was time to tack up again, Fly threw his head about every time she tried to get the bridle on, and while all the other girls calmly trotted off to the centre of the ring, Ruth was left fighting and dancing round in circles by the hedge. But the instructress came over and, with the same cheerful nonchalance that Major Banks had used, offered help.

'Little beggar, aren't you?' she chided Fly, and had the bridle on instantly. Then she said, 'Nice pony. New, is he?'

'It's his first Pony Club meeting.'

'They all have to learn.' Ruth's only consolation lay in the fact that nobody seemed to think that her troubles were anything out of the ordinary.

When she got home, Ted, Ron, and Peter were eating beans on toast in the kitchen. Ruth came in feeling exhausted. With an excess of chivalry Ron offered to hot up the beans for her, and Ruth was able to flop down at the table and pour herself a cup of tea.

'How was it?' Ted asked.

'Oh, bits were all right," Ruth said cautiously. She felt she had learned a lot, if only a more exact knowledge of what she could do. 'It's those gymkhana games,' she added. 'We did games in the afternoon. Fly just doesn't know about games.'

'Fly's always playing games.'

'Not these sort of games. Bending and things. You have to go in and out down a row of bamboo canes. All the good ponies canter and turn on a sixpence and come back again. Fly just trod on them, or missed them altogether, and went half-way across the field before I could turn him round.'

Ruth ate her baked beans, and told the humiliating story of how Fly had bolted across the field and she had had to be rescued by Major Banks. Ted and Ron made sympathetic faces, and passed a few facetious remarks about horseplay, then went back to discussing a magazine which they had laid out on the table showing the specifications of the latest Metisse frame. Ruth reached for the sugar, and realized that Peter was watching her, saying nothing as usual. In her preoccupied state she had forgotten all about him and now, seeing his politely inexpressive look, she wanted to throw the sugar-basin at him. She hated him for knowing so much, and herself for knowing so little.

Ron pushed his chair back and closed the magazine. 'You won't go again, I take it?' he said to Ruth.

'I jolly well will,' Ruth said fiercely.

Ron grinned. 'A martyr to the cause.'

The next day was hot again, with a sweet breeze blowing up

from the river. It was the sort of day to be utterly content, yet Ruth could not feel it. She was all ruffled up inside, and rode down over the stubble fields to the creek without hearing a single note of the skylarks' music cascading from the sky, or the summer purr of the distant combines. The tide was high and Peter was drifting about in an old inner tube with another boy from the estate. They kept tipping each other out, ducking and spluttering. Ruth rode along the sea-wall and watched them, aloof from their enjoyment. She knew she was in a bad mood, and felt no better when she saw Pearl trotting down the hill towards her on Milky Way. Milky Way was trotting lame, as she often did. The ground was very hard, and Ruth frowned. She rode off down the wall and went to meet her.

'Hullo,' Pearl said. 'What was it like? Do you know how to make your pony behave now?'

Ruth's eyes sparked. She felt anger fizzing up inside her, but was very careful when she spoke.

'I know enough not to ride my pony when it's lame,' she said shortly.

'Riding her doesn't make it any worse,' Pearl said. She was holding Milky Way in so tightly that the mare took a step backwards. Ruth looked at the perfect animal, her gleaming white coat, the flexed neck with the fine mane blowing out in the breeze, the black Arab eyes and wide nostrils, like a horse in an old painting, and felt her bad mood pricking her like a pair of spurs. What could you say to anyone like Pearl? she wondered in despair. Pearl's long hair blew out; she wore a white polo-necked jersey and spotless jodhpurs. Ruth hated her.

They rode on together. 'What did you do?' Pearl asked, and Ruth told her, leaving out all the humiliating bits.

'It sounds terribly dull. And do you mean to say that Fly really did all those things, bending and all that? I didn't think he could.' Pearl's pale green eyes slid round to look at Ruth, slyly provoking.

'Oh, didn't you?' Ruth said sharply. 'Well, he did.' Under her breath, and to herself, she added, 'After a fashion.'

'Let's canter,' said Pearl.

Not wanting to continue the conversation, Ruth cantered, seething, after Pearl. Pearl did a large circle of the field and Fly-by-Night followed, snatching at his bit, bouncing horribly. Ruth remembered the girls at the Pony Club cantering small circles, very collected, very slow. She lifted her face up to the hot sun and knew that, today, nothing would please her. Her bad mood had been encouraged by Pearl. Pearl rode with her toes down and gaps under her knees. Major Banks would shout at her, Ruth thought.

Milky Way pulled up, dropping one shoulder, on the path that ran up to the sea-wall. Peter and his friend were lying on the sea-wall, sucking grass. The friend had a transistor playing. The inappropriate row, all mixed up with the skylarks, exacerbated Ruth's ill temper.

'Let's go back across here,' Pearl said. She hauled Milky Way round so that she faced a broken gap in the fence that ran up from the sea-wall, separating the grassy ride from a field that had been recently combined. The straw bales were still lying on the red-gold stubble. Pearl stopped beside the gap and turned round to Ruth. 'After you,' she said maliciously.

Pearl knew perfectly well that Fly-by-Night would not jump the gap without a lead from Milky Way. She sat there, grinning, looking at Ruth, and Ruth knew that she was being paid out for lying about Fly-by-Night's prowess at the Pony Club. Ruth realized the justice of the situation, and the neatness of Pearl's trap, and knew she was helpless. If she was to turn up the path and say, 'I'm going home this way,' it would be as obvious an admission of failure as if she went through with the fiasco of trying to make Fly-by-Night jump.

Pearl said in a loud, clear voice, 'I bet you my new pair of jodhpurs your pony won't jump that fence without Milky leading.'

Ruth almost snorted with rage. She would gladly have seen Pearl drop dead in that moment. All her bottled anger and frustration came to boiling-point, and she snached Fly-by-Night's head up from the grass with a wrench that was worthy of Pearl herself. She looked at the gap, which consisted of a bar about two feet off the ground, and a tiny ditch, and knew that Fly-by-Night would no more jump it for her than take off and fly, but such was her blind anger that she was no longer capable of retiring from the argument. She turned Fly-by-Night round so that he was facing the gap and pressed him forward.

'Hey, Ruth!'

As Fly-by-Night, sensing what was in store for him, was already going sideways instead of forward, Ruth had no difficulty in stopping him at the interruption. She looked up and saw Peter coming down the sea-wall, still sucking his grass. He came over to her and said in a low voice, 'That was a jolly good offer. Get off.'

Ruth just stared at him.

'They're Moss Bros.,' Peter said. 'Come on, let me have him.'

Ruth slid out of the saddle, too amazed to say anything. Peter took the reins out of her hand, and Fly-by-Night stood like a rock while he mounted, ears pricked up. The stirrup-leathers were too short, but Peter just crossed the irons over the front of the saddle.

'I say,' Pearl said. 'That's not fair.'

Peter turned Fly round so that he was facing the gap

squarely and grinned at Pearl. 'You said the pony. We've got witnesses.' With no indications to Fly at all that Ruth could see, he then put him straight into a canter and jumped the gap. On the other side he pulled up, turned on a sixpence and cameback, jumping it again and pulling up beside Pearl.

'One pair of jodhpurs,' he said.

Pearl was white with anger. 'You cheated!' she said furiously. 'You've got nothing to do with it! I was talking to Ruth!'

'You said "I bet your pony won't jump",' Peter said. 'You didn't say anything about the rider. Isn't that right, Biffy?' he called up to his friend with the transistor.

'That's what she said,' Biffy agreed.

'You owe Ruth those jods, then. And if you don't give them to her, we'll come up and debag you in person.'

'Oh, you beast! My father would throw you out!'

'I bet your father doesn't make bets he doesn't keep. You jolly well owe Ruth those pants, and I'll tell him so. And you shouldn't ride a pony as lame as that. I'll tell him that, too.'

'You mind your own business, you interfering—oh!' Words failed Pearl. She wrenched Milky Way round and disappeared up the hill at a flat gallop, all pale flying hair and tail. Ruth stood watching, acutely happy. Even Biffy's transistor now seemed to be playing celestial music.

'There,' said Peter, looking rather pleased. 'That showed her.' He slid off Fly-by-Night. 'You make sure she sticks to what she said.'

'Look,' Ruth said, 'how did you get him to jump that?'

Peter looked surprised. 'What do you mean?'

'He won't jump it for me.'

'Oh, they get to know what they can get away with, I suppose.'

'You mean it's me, all the things he won't do?'

111

'Well, I don't know.'

'Look, I won't ask you ever again, but just this once, while you're in the mood, would you just see if you can get him to jump that again, and go up the field in and out of the bales, as if it's bending, and canter a circle and—oh, you know, the Pony Club sort of things? Will you?'

'Well, if you like.'

Peter got on again, and lengthened the stirrups. 'One dressage display coming up.'

Fly-by-Night went over the gap again, jumping big, his ears pricked up. To Ruth, never having seen him being ridden before, he looked magnificent, all shining bounce and jauntiness. He flexed his neck to Peter's hands, carrying himself with the same boldness that she had once admired in Toadhill Flax. Peter seemed not to do anything, just sit there, but Fly-by-Night went up the lines of bales, in and out, at a canter, without once poking his nose or even attempting to run out. At the top he turned and came back, first at an extended trot, then at a collected trot, then at a slow, collected canter. Opposite the gap once more, Peter cantered him in a circle on the correct leg, then changed direction and sent him off in a circle on the other leg. He then halted and got him to stand out, show-wise, all collected and square on his four legs. He reined back four paces, did a turn on the forehand, and jumped back over the gap to halt in front of Ruth.

'There. I'd do a levade, too, but I haven't got my cocked hat with me,' he said.

Biffy shouted from the sea-wall, 'When you've finished assing about down there, we were on our way to look for a Comma, if you remember.'

Peter got off again and handed Ruth the reins. 'He's nice,' he said. 'Reminds me of Toad, only smaller.' He picked another piece of grass to suck and ambled away to join Biffy.

112

Half-way up the sea-wall he turned and said, 'Those jods are yours, remember. Biffy'll be a witness.'

'Come on,' Biffy said. 'Wasting blooming time with girls' stuff.'

The two of them disappeared over the sea-wall, and the strains of the transistor faded away across the saltings. Fly-by-Night put his head down and started to graze, as if he had never seen grass before, and Ruth stood looking at him, in a daze. She felt as if something had come out of the sky and hit her. There was nobody in sight at all, just herself and Fly-by-Night on the edge of the stubble-field, and the distant hedges all shimmering in the heat.

'Fly-by-Night,' she said.

Fly flicked an eye at her, pulling at the grass. Then, just like a pony in one of her books, he lifted his head and gave a little flutter of his nostrils, and rubbed his head against her arm in a friendly way. Ruth felt weepy all of a sudden, elated and weepy altogether, in a strange, dazed way.

'It's the heat,' she said to herself, and mounted Fly-by-Night. He cleared the gap in one bound, and cantered away up the stubble-field.

The next morning, when Ruth did her paper round, she found a brown paper parcel on the doorstep of 'The Place', addressed to herself. Inside were the jodhpurs, with the Moss Bros. label still new and unsoiled.

11 Riding at Hillingdon

One afternoon at the end of August when Ruth came in from her ride she found her mother in the kitchen drinking cups of tea with Mrs. Challoner.

'Do you know where Peter is?' Mrs. Hollis asked Ruth.

'He's down the creek somewhere, I think. Do you want him?'

The two women looked at each other warily, and Mrs. Hollis said, 'No hurry, I suppose.'

Mrs. Challoner, looking relieved, said, 'I'll leave it to you to tell him, then?'

'Yes, all right.'

When Mrs. Challoner had gone Ruth said nervously to her mother, 'Tell him what?'

'That his father's married a Neapolitan opera-singer.'

Ruth looked at her mother to see if she was joking, but she did not look particularly amused.

'Do you mean it? It doesn't sound—er—well—' Ruth was at a loss. Neapolitan opera-singers did not ride horses, nor stand in cold collecting-rings in sheepskin-lined jackets calling out the numbers.

'They want Peter to go home.'

'Oh, no!'

'He'd have to go back soon, in any case,' her mother said. 'I only hope he'll find a new mother an added attraction.'

Amazingly, Peter did. 'What's she like?' he asked cautiously.

'All Mrs. Challoner told me, dear, is that she's rather fat and speaks no English at all, but smiles all the time.'

Ruth listened to the conversation, wondering if it was real. It didn't sound like the sort of thing that actually happened to ordinary people. Afterwards, when she was alone with Peter, she said to him, 'Do you mind?'

'It can't be worse than it was before,' he said.

'Why, what was it like before?'

'Well, at least someone smiling all the time will be nice to have around, won't it?'

He did not say any more, but his remark seemed very reasonable to Ruth.

She had known that he was going back when his father came home, but had put off thinking about it. It was not that he had, in fact, helped a great deal practically in schooling Fly-by-Night since the day he had ridden him down by the creek, but his having shown Ruth what was possible had helped her immeasurably. Her confidence had increased, which Fly-by-Night had seemed to sense, and the better the pony did for her the more sure she became, so that she felt that their mutual progress was like a snowball, steadily building up. They still had plenty of bad patches to put it all in perspective, but these did not cast Ruth down with the same force as they had earlier in the year. She was more philosophic about it all.

'You'll get fat at this rate,' Ron said approvingly. 'Nothing to worry about.'

The Pony Club no longer held her in awe, expecting the worst. After two or three more times, Fly-by-Night stopped his whinnying and displays of astonishment, and settled down to doing what he was told (even if it was only because all the other ponies were doing the same thing). Ruth made some tentative friends, but none who lived within riding distance, so that her love-hate relationship with Pearl continued as far as riding out was concerned.

'Why do you go out with that horrible girl?' Peter asked her.

'Because she calls for me. And she *was* honest about the jodhpurs.' Ruth felt bound to defend poor Pearl.

'She couldn't have wriggled out of that,' Peter said. 'She made the offer in a loud enough voice, so that everyone would have to take notice.'

'Take notice of me not being able to make Fly jump the gap.'

'Yes, well, we fixed her, didn't we?' Peter said with great satisfaction. 'Has she got the vet yet?'

'No.'

Milky Way was still a source of grief to Ruth. 'I would give anything,' she said, 'to own Milky Way.'

'She's not worth anything, the way she is,' Peter said.

'That's not the point. It's her nature that I love.'

Peter said, 'There's only one pony that I've ever liked. I mean liked as—as—oh, you know. More than just something to ride. A pony that was like somebody.'

'Who was that? Woodlark?'

'Woodlark? Ugh! No, it was Toad.'

116

'Toadhill Flax? What happened to him?'

'Dad sold him,' Peter said. 'He said I could have him for my own, then a week later someone offered a good price for him, and he sold him.'

'Your father's horrible!'

Peter grinned. 'But I've got a lovely mother—a big, fat, enormous, spaghetti-eating, smiling opera-singer.'

Ruth was shocked.

Peter went home, and Ruth did not see him until she went back to school. Even then they did not have much opportunity to talk, but Ruth gathered that Peter thought his home vastly improved. 'My father's a new man,' he said. 'You won't recognize him. He's taking singing lessons. And we have spaghetti every day. Truly. All oozing with lovely, greasy gravy, and garlic in it.' Ruth did not know whether he was making it up, or whether he meant it. It still just did not sound quite real to her. She went home and told her mother, and her mother was pleased.

'Just what the place needed, I should imagine. Mrs. Challoner told me, when she first went there, that the house was just like an extension of the stables, all littered with gear and sale catalogues, and linseed on the cooker, stinking the place out. No fires, just a bit of old cheese in the pantry. No wonder Peter got fed up.'

Ruth missed having him at home dreadfully. They all did. Ted, not yet fit enough to go back to work, was morose with boredom. The first coal of the winter was delivered, and Ruth heard, with a familiar feeling of dread, the mutterings of her father over the bill. She realized that he had got steadily quieter over the past year, more and more worried looking, and less given to making the jokes that had made them all laugh. She heard him say to her mother, 'This winter will find us out. I really think we'll have to move before the next one. But heavens know where to.'

'A flat would do us, now the children are growing up,' Mrs. Hollis said.

Ruth could not bear to listen. She did not think anything so bad could happen. 'That's what you thought when Ted had his accident,' she reminded herself. 'And that happened.'

Ted went to the doctor to get permission to go back to work, but the doctor would not hear of it. 'Come the New Year, and we'll consider it,' the doctor said. Ted, who was still under treatment at the hospital for the injury to his back, was not surprised, but his frustration increased. Always an active person, the enforced idleness came hard, and the fact that his disability was adding substantially to the family's financial difficulties gave him a guilt complex that made him gloomy and pessimistic.

Ruth, having gained new confidence with Fly-by-Night, now found that her season of content was doomed.

'It can't happen!' she said desperately to Ron. 'I can't give him up now, when everything is beginning to come right!' She did not dare let her parents see how much it mattered, because she knew that they had enough to bother about as it was. There was only Ron, the universal comforter, whose presence invariably cheered Ted, and whom everyone was pleased to see.

'Well, it hasn't happened yet,' Ron said steadily. 'And if you do move to somewhere without a field, perhaps Peter could help you out? Your parents did a lot for him, after all. Mr. McNair might keep Fly-by-Night for you.'

'But without paying? I couldn't afford to pay.'

'What your mother did for Peter is worth years of a pony's keep.'

'But, if it's a flat, that means a town, and we'll be miles away from Hillingdon—how shall I be able to go over and ride him often enough?' Even to Ron, Ruth could not explain that she would have to see Fly-by-Night often, almost every day, or life would have no point at all. In fact, she could not imagine herself without the pony. Life without Fly-by-Night was like a thick fog in her imagination. It was a nothing. Even sensible Ron would not understand how utterly committed she was.

His idea was a straw, and Ruth clutched at it. One night her parents drafted out an advertisement to put in the paper, to sell the house, and the next day Ruth waylaid Peter at school, after lunch, and told him what was happening.

'I'm sure we could keep Fly-by-Night for you,' Peter said gravely. 'I know my father wouldn't mind.' He pondered, and looked at Ruth's tight, miserable face. 'It'll be difficult for you, getting over to ride him.'

Ruth nodded. 'About three hours' bike-riding, to a couple of hours' pony-riding.' It was better than selling him, but the prospect was heart-chilling.

Peter grimaced. 'Rather you than me.' He paused, then said, 'Look, why don't you come over on Saturday and see my father about it? Come over on Fly, then you can try him round our course.'

Ruth's heart leapt at the invitation. Simultaneously she thought of all the snags. 'It's a lot of road, to get to you. He's not shod.'

'Haven't you had him shod yet? Why ever not?'

'I can't afford it,' Ruth muttered.

'Oh, but you must,' Peter said. 'Then you can come up whenever you like, and use our jumps. I bet you won't move for ages yet, if your parents are only just writing out the advertisement.'

Ruth was silent.

Peter said, 'If you ride him up on Saturday, you can leave him at our place, because the smith's coming next Monday. Then he can be shod with ours, and you can take him back again afterwards. You won't have to pay anything. How about that?'

Ruth was silent again. The prospect was so inviting that her puritan streak made her feel she must refuse. Then she thought of Ron's sense, and grinned, and said, 'Yes, that would be marvellous.'

The house advertisement was in the paper on the Friday and on Saturday morning, as Ruth left home on Fly-by-Night, a man and a woman had already arrived to view. Ruth rode away down the concrete road, trying to keep her mind on the marvellous day that lay before her, but her stupid wits kept wandering, and all she could think of were the grassy tracks down to the creek where the skylarks sang, and the red-gold stubble where Fly-by-Night had cantered through August and September. 'Don't be *stupid*,' she told herself. 'What's the good of thinking of that?'

Now, early November, the fields were all ploughed again, and the elms baring, like ink drawings against the sky. The tarmac gleamed with rain. Fly-by-Nigth's coat was thickening, the frosty roan working over the movement of his shoulders as his unshod hoofs padded along the verge. 'When you come back,' Ruth told him, 'you will clatter. You'll frighten the wits out of yourself.'

But today he was good, and they reached the McNair drive without incident. Ruth felt Fly stiffen with excitement as he smelt the other horses. Peter was in the yard waiting for her.

'We'll put him in a box for now, and you can come indoors and meet my big fat momma. Then this afternoon we can ride.'

'What, you too?'

'Why not?'

Ruth realized that the chocolate-éclair sessions must have had good effect after all. 'Fly-by-Night's never been in a 'loose-box before—at least, not that I know of,' she said. 'I don't suppose he'll like it.'

'Time he learnt,' Peter said. 'Do you want to look at the horses?'

Ruth felt herself shiver with pure pleasure. A place like McNair's, with Peter now her personal friend, was her idea of paradise. The boxes were all immaculate, full of clean straw and shining animals. Fly-by-Night, appeased with a large net of hay, stood looking about him with amazed, excited eyes—no less amazed and excited than Ruth's. She followed Peter down the yard, looking in at each half-door, and Peter told her about each inmate. 'Jason. He's nice, but been spoilt.' Jason was a fourteen-and-a-half-hand chestnut with a lovely head and a bold eye. 'And this is Prairie Fire. He's won two point-to-points. My eldest brother is riding him in a National Hunt race next week.' Prairie Fire was dark bay, a raking, powerful gelding with scars on his legs. 'You can't stop him once he's going. But can he go! This grey is Seashell. She's as mild as milk, lady's hunter. And this is Rustum. Half-Arab, nice, very green . . . ugh, Woodlark. You pretty little devil! This is beastly Woodlark.'

'Why is she so beastly?'

'You can have a ride on her, if you like. You'll find out. She's got a nasty female mind.'

'Better than a nasty male mind.'

'Oh, no, give me a gelding any day.'

Ruth followed Peter round to the house, in a warm, horsy dream. The house was warm, filled with delicious cooking smells. In the kitchen, Mr. McNair was sitting in front of a blazing fire, reading *Horse and Hound* and drinking coffee, and at the cooker stood the Neapolitan opera-singer. Ruth thought she was like a great sun. Well-being emanated from her like the warmth from the fire. She beamed at Ruth, and immediately produced steaming mugs of cocoa, and

Ruth was fascinated by the vastness of her; yet she was so neat and quick and strong with it, and so happy. She sang while she cooked, and spoke in torrents of beautiful Italian, which nobody understood, but Mr. McNair and Peter nodded and smiled and said, 'Si, si,' and after a little while Ruth found herself doing the same. Ruth could see the change that had been wrought in Peter's father, for he had an air of contentment about him like a domestic cat on the hearth-rug. Ruth would not have recognized the same man who had nagged Peter on the day of the Hunter Trials. After a delicious lunch, Ruth left the house almost regretfully to go riding with Peter. She had offered to wash up, but had been refused with a cascade of shocked surprise and an embrace.

'Nice, isn't she?' Peter said, as they went back to the stables. 'You can't imagine the change she's made in everything.'

Ruth looked at Peter, remembered the night he had arrived in her own home, pale and silent, and thought how strangely things worked out: now it was her turn to be hurt by what was happening, and Peter's turn to be made happy. They seemed to have no control over anything at all.

Peter decided to ride his beastly Woodlark, because he said she needed it, so they saddled the two ponies and rode side by side across McNair's fields to the woods beyond. There were no woods where Ruth lived, and as the ponies left the open fields and turned on to a peaty track that led away into an unfamiliar, cathedral-like gloom, Ruth was aware of a new dimension in her riding. Fly-by-Night's hoofs rustled in brittle leaves; trailers of wild clematis tangled in her hair. It was silent and secret. When a pair of wood-pigeons clattered suddenly, heavily, out of the branches above their heads, she was as startled as Fly-by-Night, and shied with him in spirit. Peter turned and laughed, and Ruth saw Woodlark break into a trot and start twisting through the trees, Peter bending low to miss the branches, yet quite easy and still in the saddle. Fly-by-Night, anxious not to be left behind, followed eagerly, and Ruth felt herself whipped and whacked by the trees. She bent down like Peter, but bounced and slithered and bit her tongue. She had no control over Fly-by-Night at all.

'A bit different from the sea-wall!' Peter said, pulling up to wait.

Fly-by-Night barged into Woodlark's quarters, but Peter turned the mare instantly, before she had time to think about kicking. 'We've made a Hunter Trials sort of course through the rides here. All the jumps are very low. I bet Fly-by-Night will do it, if Woodlark gives him a lead. Do you want to try it?'

Ruth, getting her breath back, nodded. She was frightened, and longing to do it at the same time. She felt as if the trees were pressing down on her. It was like being indoors. There was a cracking of dry twigs and Woodlark was away, cantering over the thick, soft humus. Ruth felt Fly-by-Night go, without her telling him, and she sat there, head down, her throat dry with fright, but all her instincts up over the jumps ahead of herself. This, she recognized, was the very stuff of her dreams: Peter giving Fly-by-Night a lead and herself learning what it would be like at Brierley.

The jumps came at her at all angles; she just got a warning in time by the flick of Woodlark's black tail ahead of her. Fly-by-Night crashed through regardless, carrying away loads of brush on his thrashing hoofs. Ruth had a vision of Woodlark disappearing suddenly, as if over a precipice, then herself teetering on the edge of a peaty bank, looking down on Peter. She saw Woodlark stretched out, bounding away from her, then she was flying through the air as Fly-by-Night plunged in pursuit. Amazingly, at the bottom, she landed back in the saddle, although she was convinced that she had come down the bank quite independently of her pony. There was a jolt; she clutched a handful of mane, and stayed with him as he went over a log and away down a stinging ride, hoof-fuls of peat from Woodlark's hoofs flinging up in his face. For a moment she had time to enjoy it, the muffled ground running beneath, the smell of wet bark and pungent leaf, and the sourness of fungus and decay; then Peter had turned right-handed ahead of her and they were flying a bank into a thicket. There was running water below, and the clutching of brambles. Ruth shut her eyes. Fly-by-Night stopped suddenly.

'Still there?' she heard Peter say, and they were out on the edge of the open fields again, pulling up on familiar slippery grass. Woodlark's nostrils were red as she curvetted to a standstill, all feminine elegance, Peter's hands taking her up, strong but not rough. Fly-by-Night stopped in three bounds, tearing up streamers of turf. Ruth landed up his neck.

'Oh, heavens!' Ruth muttered. How did Peter have time to think? she wondered. How would she ever do it, alone?

'Lots of that is what you want,' Peter said. 'It's very good for getting them handy. If you came up every week-end, he'd soon be going round without any trouble.'

'Oh, if I could—!'

'But why not?'

Wracked with fears, longings, and doubts, Ruth left Fly-by-Night in the McNair paddocks and cycled home on Peter's bike. She had half-expected to see the removal van outside and all their possessions on the pavement, but when she asked her mother, 'Did they buy it?' Mrs. Hollis looked at her in amazement, and laughed. 'Gracious me, you're in a hurry! We've had three lots of people to see, but nobody's falling over themselves to give us a cheque. These things take time, as a rule.' Ruth, without Fly-by-Night in the garden, felt bereaved. 'This is what it will be like if we move,' she thought. What good would a pony be to her half across the country, a Saturday pony? A pony was for talking to and for looking at out of your bedroom window, and riding even if you only had half an hour before tea. What good would Fly-by-Night be, left in a paddock, even a McNair paddock, if nobody bothered with him except at week-ends? Now, just when her dreams of Peter helping her were coming true, satisfaction was bludgeoned by all the other circumstances. Ruth wept. 'What's the matter with you?' her mother asked.

'It's her age,' Ted said, which was a family joke to explain the unpredictable.

Fly-by-Night was shod and Ruth rode him home. In his field that night he whinnied for his lost companions, and roamed up and down the hedges. 'He'd have friends if he lived at McNair's,' Ruth thought. 'But he wouldn't have me.' She didn't think he would mind terribly, not having her, but she minded. She wept again. Her mother gave her two aspirins and a hot lemon.

Peter was right about the house not being sold very quickly. Ruth, Ted and Elizabeth got used to putting everything away and keeping the place excruciatingly tidy for the couples who would call inconveniently in the evenings and poke round their bedrooms and in the airing-cupboard and the bathroom. Mr. and Mrs. Hollis went to look at flats, and came home with long faces, saying nothing. Because she was going to leave it, Ruth loved the grassy tracks down to the creek more and more. The stubble was ploughed, snow fell on the saltings and piled up in big drifts against the sea-wall. The winter was as bad as the summer had been good, and there were only a few Saturdays when Ruth was able to ride over to Hillingdon. Even then the wood was bogged down and the ground too wet for jumping. She would hack through the fields with Peter and they would come back into the house for platefuls of steaming risotto round the fire, then Ruth would hurry home along the darkening roads, wincing at the sluicings from passing cars. But Fly-by-Night had enough to eat, because Mr. McNair came down in the estate car and left sacks of pony-nuts and some bales of good hay.

One Wednesday evening a middle-aged couple who had looked at the house earlier called back and left Mr. Hollis a deposit on it. 'They don't want to move in any great hurry,' Ruth heard him say, 'but I suppose we'd better decide what we're going to do.'

'The flat over the butcher's shop, next door to Woolworth's was the best of the last batch,' Mrs. Hollis replied.

Ruth felt sick. Her parents asked her if she would like to go and see it with them, but she shook her head, white and silent. Ted went, and came back and said, 'It's all right. There's a good yard round the back for a motor bike. Near Ron, too.'

It was snowing softly. In the field Fly-by-Night's back was melting the snow as it fell, but his roan made it look as if it was lying on him. He whinnied impatiently for his nuts, shaking drops of moisture off his muzzle hairs. Ruth stroked his hard neck. Under its roughness, his coat was shining with Mr. McNair's good feeding, and he was fit, and his hoofs shapely from the blacksmith. Ruth went up the garden and cried again, over the washing-up, and her mother said sharply, 'Ruth, for heaven's sake! At least you can *keep* him—what more do you want?' But the flat next to Woolworth's was fifteen miles from Hillingdon.

Three days later, when the thaw set in, Ron called. As he unwound all his layers and wrappings in the kitchen, his nose shining red in his good-natured, unhandsome face, Ruth put the kettle on to make him a cup of tea.

'There was an ambulance going down the lane at the

bottom. Asked me for Mr. Lacey's. So I went along to show 'em the way. He's got his daughter over there from London, but she said the cold was too much for him. He's got pneumonia. He looked bad. I wouldn't be surprised if that's the finish of him.'

'Oh, poor Mr. Lacey!' Ruth said. 'I didn't know.' And even as she spoke the words, an unworthy thought came into her head. She looked at Ron and saw that the unworthy thought was in his head, too. Flushing slightly, she turned away to fetch the tea-caddy. They neither of them said anything more about Mr. Lacey.

It snowed again the next week, and Ruth, unable to resist the temptation, went down the lane and walked up Mr. Lacey's garden path. The pear trees, loaded with snow, seemed to lean against the dilapidated lean-to kitchen. Big puddles lay on the stone flags inside. Ruth could not see her mother there, somehow. With set face she peered in through the living-room windows. The ceilings were cracked and flakes of plaster lay on the carpet like indoor snow. She could see the narrow staircase curling up, and the brick floor. At the back there was a conservatory with a vine in it. Ruth turned her head away and walked on down the garden. The old fruit trees made arched roofs of snow over her head; every move on her part brought a rushing avalanche. Beyond the trees were the old sheds, a line of them, with sagging roofs, cluttered about with old water-butts and rolls of wire-netting and rotted rabbit hutches. Beyond again, a gate, and two acres of virgin snow, quilted with birds' feet, stretching towards the marshes. Ruth stood in the snow and squeezed her face up with longing. 'Oh, God, *please*! Please could it happen? He needn't die; he could just go and live with his daughter.'

But when she got home her mother said Mr. Lacey had died that afternoon.

12 A Day of Decisions

'Oh, the messiness of it!' Ruth said to Ron. 'The not knowing. The misery of it!'

She sat at the kitchen table, with the Hunter Trials entry form in front of her. There was a month to go, and a smell of spring in the air outside.

'Woe, woe, woe!' Ted wailed. 'Oh, misery me!' He reached over for a box of crisps that stood on the table and ducked his hand in.

'Hasn't she made her mind up *yet*?' Ron said.

'Oh, reely, I don't know what to do for the best, Mr.

'Ollis,' said Ted in a mimicking voice. 'George says sell the place and Edie says keep it, it'll be worth a lot of money for building one of these days. And our Ada says we could use it for a summer cottage. And Joe says keep it in the family; our Tom has hankerings after being a farmer, and he's only a year more to do at school and we could set him up in tomatoes, like, if we had a bit of ground. And our Ethel says—'

'Oh, shut up,' said Ruth. She wanted to buy Mr. Lacey's house so badly that she could not bear Ted to joke about it. Her father wanted to buy it, too, and her mother, not at all enthusiastic, at least agreed that it could be made into something habitable. But their own house was sold and in six weeks they were going to have to move out, and Mr. Lacey's only daughter could not make up her mind whether to accept Mr. Hollis's offer or not. Ruth prayed for her every night, prayed for the woman's addled mind to clear, for her to agree to sell it. If it had not been for the Hunter Trials coming so close, so that they now filled her mind largely to the exclusion of everything else, she did not think she could have stood the suspense for so long. Mr. Lacey's place was paradise, and Ruth felt as if she were standing at the gates, looking in, and Mr. Lacey's daughter was fumbling in her large untidy handbag for the key. For weeks and weeks she had been fumbling. Ruth had gone thin again, and edgy, and her father said, 'It doesn't matter that much, Ruth,' as he had once said about buying a pony, but this time he did not say it with any great conviction, because he, too, wanted to buy Mr. Lacey's cottage almost as much as Ruth. 'You really could do things with a place like that,' he would say, standing dreamily in front of the fire, jingling his money in his pocket. 'You'll need to, believe me,' Mrs. Hollis would say, rather sharply. 'I'll sweep it up for you,' Elizabeth told her. 'It only wants dusting. It's a nice house.'

Ted, looking for another motor bike to buy with his insurance money from the accident, had earmarked one of the sheds for a workshop. He was back at work again, and happy. Ruth had hoped that even if they didn't get Mr. Lacey's house they might have stayed where they were now that Ted was working again, but her parents were not going back on their decision to move.

'We must get a cheaper place,' Mr. Hollis said firmly. 'I'm not changing my mind.'

He did not like his work very much, Ruth knew, so she supposed it must be a poor life for him to work without joy merely to pay for necessities like a roof and food, and with no money left over for having a bit of fun. Sometimes in the summer he would walk down to the river to watch the sailing, and come back very quiet, and rather short-tempered. Ruth knew he would like a boat, although he never said so. Even a holiday, which they had not had now for five years.

But Ruth, when she got to thinking about it too much, had only to turn her mind to the Brierley Hunter Trials to know what real apprehension was. The days were drawing inexorably nearer. If she had thought—as she had thought last year—that she had no chance at all of getting Fly-by-Night round the course, she would not have bothered; she would have admitted her failure. But she knew now—thanks to the McNair schooling grounds—that he had a chance. He was not hopeless. If he was in the right mood he would go like Woodlark herself. Peter no longer had to give him a lead. Anyone else but herself, Ruth thought, would be looking forward to the date with a pleasurable anticipation, but she could only face it with near panic. But she was going.

'Will you be going?' she had asked Peter at school.

'Oh, I might. When is it?' Peter said, very off-hand. Ruth

told him the date and he said, 'If there's nothing else to do I might.'

When Ruth rode out with Pearl, Fly-by-Night could give the Arab mare a lead over the gap into the stubble field. Pearl, unwilling to accede that Fly-by-Night had improved, said, 'It's Milly being off colour, with this stiff leg of hers.'

'Haven't you got the vet *yet*?' Ruth asked her.

Pearl shook her head, but looked rather chastened. 'I will,' she said.

Two days later she came round to Ruth's on her bicycle and said, 'What do you think? Mr. Richards came round today to look at Milly, and he said she's got navicular. Apparently it's incurable, so Daddy's buying me a new pony.'

Ruth looked at Pearl in astonishment.

'But what will you do with Milly?'

Pearl shrugged. 'I don't know. She's useless, according to Mr. Richards. He said it never gets better, and the pony stumbles a lot and is unsafe to ride. So Daddy says I can have a new one!' She was obviously far more excited about the new pony than concerned about the fate of Milky Way. Ruth looked at her coldly.

'Will you keep Milky Way?'

'Mr. Richards says we should breed a foal from her. But we shall want the stable for the new pony. I don't know what we'll do.'

'A foal . . .?' Ruth's eyes opened wide at this entrancing idea. 'You won't sell her? You *can't* sell her! Oh, it would be lovely to breed a foal!'

'Yes, but I want something to ride, don't I?'

At school the next day Ruth reported to Peter. 'What is navicular anyway?' she asked him. 'Is it as bad as she makes out?'

'Yes, it gets gradually worse with age, so a horse with

131

navicular disease isn't really any good. It's always liable to go lame. It's a sort of inflammation of one of the bones in the foot. My father wouldn't touch a horse if he thought it had navicular.'

'I wonder what they'll do?' Ruth mused.

'They could sell her to someone for breeding. She'd still be quite valuable—that's the big advantage with mares, when something like that crops up.'

Ruth drifted through the next lesson in a dream, choosing a sire worthy of Milky Way, seeing the mare grazing peacefully under summer trees with her Arab foal. Her head was full of dreams: of Fly-by-Night winning the Hunter Trials, of her father buying Mr. Lacey's house . . . 'Ruth Hollis, stop biting your nails,' the teacher said acidly.

There was a fortnight to go to the date for Brierley . . . a week. Ruth started to worry about getting there, because it was a long way to hack, all on the roads. Her mother was worried about moving, because they had nowhere, as yet, to move to at the end of the month. 'You must give that woman an ultimatum,' she said to her husband. 'We can't wait for her to make up her mind for ever.' 'All right,' said Mr. Hollis. Ted was completely involved in buying a new motor bike, going round looking at machines with Ron every evening. Pearl's father was driving all over the countryside looking at expensive ponies for Pearl.

'What a mess it is all at once,' Ruth thought again. 'So many things going on, everything so untidy . . .' But just then, in her mind, only the Saturday of the Hunter Trials mattered. All the other things could wait until afterwards. Triumph or disaster would happen on Saturday, and all the other things would sort themselves out, too, afterwards . . . triumph or disaster. 'One thing at a time,' Ruth thought.

On the Thursday Peter said to her at school, quite casually, 'We're taking Woodlark to Brierley on Saturday. We'll pick you up if you like. It's not out of the way.'

'Fly-by-Night, you mean? In the horse-box?' Ruth wanted to get it quite right.

'Yes. We'll take the big one.'

'Thank you. That would be a terrific help.' Ruth spoke calmly, but the offer was such a relief that she could quite easily have embraced Peter on the spot.

'By the way,' Peter grinned suddenly, 'Father-of-Pearl called yesterday, to see if we had any animals suitable for his dear daughter.'

'Oh, and did you?'

'They fancied—wait for it—get ready to laugh—you'll never guess—'

'Woodlark?'

'Right first time!' Peter was grinning. 'That's why we're taking her to Brierley, as Father-of-Pearl wants to see what she'll do. Of course, she'll go round like a bomb, so we're not worried. Father tried to tell Father-of-Pearl what an absolute beast she was, but he kept saying, "My girl's a splendid little rider. She can handle anything." So after a bit Father piped down. And Pearl was doing her uppity act, treating Father like a shop assistant, so he came in hopping mad and said, "Let them buy her, and good luck to 'em." It was a real laugh. I enjoyed every minute of it.'

Ruth could not help smiling, picturing Peter taking it all in with his non-expression on his face, not saying anything.

'If she rides Woodlark like she rides Milky Way, she'll get bucked off in double-quick time, splendid little rider and all,' Peter said.

Ruth knew that Woodlark was a pony who would stick up for herself; she was as bold, and crafty, as Milky Way was sweet and kind. Ruth had no wish that Pearl should come to a bad end, but she hoped more that Milky Way would be made happy.

'Everyone will be at Brierley on Saturday,' she thought, without enthusiasm. Besides Pearl's family, her own mother and father had said they would like to come and see her 'jump round', and Ted and Ron had said they would 'drop in'. None of this comforted Ruth at all. Now it was so close she wished desperately that it was over.

On Friday night she cleaned her tack, and groomed Fly-by-Night in the field. The weather was dry and sharp, the evening sky pink and ploughed and calm. Fly-by-Night now stood tied up without protesting, but he still did not stand in the resigned way that Ruth so desired; he still fidgeted and gnawed the post, or tried to graze. But he did not bite her any more, and he never kicked. His feet were shapely, newly-shod (at McNair's, as before), and his winter coat had thinned, and shone when the mud had been removed. 'You're not bad, for forty pounds,' Ruth said to him, and he looked at her, four-square, cocky, his little white crescent shining in the dusk. To Ruth, he looked so marvellous she felt a lump come into the throat.

That night she felt that she never slept at all, although she supposed afterwards that she must have done, on and off. She got up feeling sick, and thought how blissful it would be if she didn't have to go. 'Talk about a glutton for punishment!' Ted remarked. 'What time does the tumbril start rolling?' Ruth tried to laugh, but it was impossible.

She knew that her attitude was ridiculous, but it made no difference.

She went out and groomed Fly-by-Night again, getting the mud off his feet as best she could. The day was damp and grey, fairly warm, but not very exciting. Somewhere there was a sun that suggested it might come through later. But it had not rained again, and the ground was fairly dry. 'Thank goodness,' Ruth thought, 'I am going with the McNairs!' The thought of setting out alone made her shiver. She fed Fly-by-Night and let him loose again, and went indoors and changed into Pearl's jodphurs, and the jodphur boots and grown-out-of black jacket that Peter had lent her for the occasion. She had her own hat, shabby but serviceable, and a white school blouse and a rather frayed Pony Club tie—also Peter's. She pulled her hair back with a rubber band, and looked at herself in the mirror, and thought she looked like someone at the Horse of the Year Show. 'Hope we jump like it,' she said to her reflection, and smiled and held out her hands for the silver trophy, like a photograph in *Horse and Hound*. But there would be no silver trophy for her, however well Fly-by-Night did, because she was in the same class as Peter. It was a wild dream indeed that made her think of rosettes, but, of course, dreams will rise to anything. When she went downstairs everyone remarked how smart she looked.

'Do you want to take your sandwiches with you? Or shall we bring them in the car?' her mother asked.

'Oh, you bring them,' Ruth said, not interested in food.

'Tumbril's coming up the road now,' Ted said, from the kitchen door. Ruth gave a little shrieck and turried out to catch Fly-by-Night.

Mr. McNair came in for a cup of coffee, and Peter and Ruth boxed Fly-by-Night, with Woodlark rolling a wild white eye at him over the top of the partition, and all the neighbours peering. Peter, too, looked strangely smart in a black jacket and tie; the decorum of his garb after jeans and polo-necked jerseys with holes in the elbows, emphasized the essential seriousness of the day, and Ruth felt a little more hollow inside. 'I feel dreadful,' she said bleakly.

Peter said, 'You're mad! About a potty thing like this?

We wouldn't have bothered if Woodlark hadn't got to be shown off.'

'What if she does what she did last year?'

'Last year she was scarcely broken in! Green as grass. It was daft to try it. That's when Father was a bit off his rocker, between you and me and the gate-post.'

Mr. McNair, no longer off his rocker, came cheerfully down the garden path and said, 'Got everything, girl? Saddle and bridle aboard? All set to go?'

Ruth nodded, and squashed into the front of the horse-box between Mr. McNair and Peter. Her parents came out and waved and shouted, 'See you later!' and the horse-box rolled away down the concrete road.

'It's started,' Ruth thought, but now she felt calmer and more cheerful. After all, no worse could happen to her than happened to Peter last year, and he didn't seem to think it mattered at all. He and his father were talking about a knock in the horse-box engine.

For the third time Ruth passed through the gate on the top of Brierley Hill where the Pony Club flag fluttered out on its flag-pole by the gate. They were in plenty of time. The stewards were still trundling about in the Land-Rover and pegging out the collecting-ring.

'You can go round the course now, before we unbox the ponies,' Mr. McNair said.

'Oh, heavens, all that way!' Peter groaned. 'I know it.'

'Don't be so cocky, young fellow-me-lad,' said his father. 'How do you know it isn't quite different this year?'

Peter groaned again, but climbed down and started plodding off across the field, a white-faced Ruth at his side. Several figures could be seen in the distance, doing the same thing, climbing laboriously over the fixed timber that they all hoped to fly laultlessly and hour or two later. It was downhill from the collecting-ring, to a ditch and fairly low fixed rail in a hedge, then a long gallop up the other side to the top end of the wood.

'Take him away fast, as if you really mean it,' Peter said. 'Because a lot of them refuse the first jump, because they don't like going away from the others. Once over, you've got lots of time to get sorted out, going up the hill. Golly, what a bore, hiking all this way!'

At the top of the hill was a tiger trap into a wide ride through the wood. From this ride there was a detour through a very tangled part of the wood, over a large rotted tree-trunk, and back to the ride.

'You'll get your head knocked off here if you don't duck,' Peter said.

At the end of the ride there was a tricky jump out which involved jumping up on to a bank, and out over a ditch with a rail fixed over it.

'Woodlark takes things like this in one if I don't watch out,' Peter remarked.

After a long plod round the adjoining fields, where the jumps were all fairly straightforward, the course led back into the wood again, through the gate.

'I think I'll get off for this,' Ruth said.

'If I get off I'll never get on again,' Peter said. Ruth thought the same thing might happen to her, but decided to take the risk. 'He ought to be getting a bit weary by the time he gets this far. *If* he gets this far. He might be glad to stand.'

The course-builders had apparently decided to give the bank where Woodlark had fallen a miss this year, for from the gate the course led up a narrow twisting path through the wood to the lip of a different bank which dropped some five feet into a bit of a stream. On the far side, so that the pony had to take off straight out of the stream, a big pile of branches had been thrown across the path to make an obstacle.

'It's easier than the other bank,' Peter said. 'Not so steep.'

'Ugh,' said Ruth.

'You've done worse banks than this at home.'

'Sometimes I have,' Ruth said. 'But sometimes I haven't.'

Peter grinned. 'All part of the lovely fun,' he said.

The course led out of the wood over an easy fence and back to the start on a parallel course to the way out, down the long hill, over the ditch and another rail some fifty feet away from the first jump of the course, and back up to the collecting-ring. By the time they had got to the bottom of the hill again they had caught up with several of the girls doing the course ahead of them.

'Hullo, McNair. How many red rosettes are you picking up today?' The girl who spoke was the one with malicious eyes who Ruth always thought of as Cat's Eyes.

'More than last year, I hope,' Peter said shortly.

Cat's Eyes laughed, jeeringly. 'Of course, I'd forgotten!' She remembered now, with obvious glee. 'Instead of going over the rails and through the gate you went through the rails and over the gate.'

'Yes, that's right.'

The girl who was walking up the hill with Cat's Eyes said, 'You needn't be so clever, Mercy. The day you get over the first jump will be more memorable than the day Peter doesn't come in first.'

Ruth thought, 'Bully for you.' The girl who spoke was called Jane Withenshawe, and had come second to Peter the year Ruth had first watched. Ruth, noting that Cat's Eyes was really called Mercy, was amazed at the inaptness of it. As they made their way back to the horse-box she said, 'Why is that girl so beastly?'

'Born like it, I suppose,' Peter said. 'Jane's all right. And her pony's a cracker. Dad sold it to her three years ago.'

Jane's pony, Ruth remembered, was a bay gelding, very like Woodlark in looks, called Clipper. She remembered Peter asking Jane to pair with him, two years ago, and Jane showing in her face that she had wanted to say yes, but nobly refusing.

By the time they had unboxed the two ponies the class for the youngest children, twelve and under, had started. Ruth's stomach felt cold again as she fetched Fly-by-Night's tack and started to saddle him up. There was no sign of her family as yet, for which she was profoundly grateful, but the Pymm Jaguar was parked inside the gate. Mr. McNair went across to intercept them, in response to Peter's muttered plea.

Peter mounted Woodlark, and waited for Ruth to tighten her girths. Woodlark pivoted impatiently, flexing to her curb, her fine black mane lifting in the breeze. By comparison Fly-by-Night was sturdy, tough and masculine where the mare was all female elegance. Side by side with Peter, Ruth realized for the first time that Fly-by-Night was quite small, and that she had grown quite a lot during the last year. To give him the aids now she had to put her legs back to find his sides. She had an instant's panic: 'I am growing out of him!' but as quickly she thrust the thought from her mind. There would be time, later, to worry about that. But the thought added to her nervousness.

They walked and trotted up and down the top of the field, out of the way of the course. Ruth felt Fly-by-Night eager and bouncing beneath her, and herself stiff with nerves, her fingers like wood. Peter did not appear to be at all concerned, but he was riding Woodlark with considerable attention, not just passing the time away chatting, like most of the girls. When they eventually went down to the collecting-ring Ruth noticed several curious glances sent in her direction, and it occurred to her that being with Peter had given her a sort of standing already, although she had not done anything yet. It frightened her, and yet was a comfort at the same time. Being with Peter, she did not have to think for herself, just follow Woodlark, stand still when she stood still, and walk about when she walked about. Only, when her number was called by the steward, she would be on her own.

'I wish I could go first and get it over!' she said miserably to Peter, as the steward started checking them over. She knew she was about three-quarters of the way down the list, five behind Peter. This would be the longest hour of her life. The first girl was already away, cantering crabwise down the hill.

'We'll walk round a bit more,' Peter decided. 'It's too cold just to stand.'

Walking round a bit more, Ruth remembered all sorts of things she didn't know.

'Does the fastest round win?'

'No. Speed doesn't matter, unless you're so slow you exceed the time allowed. I shouldn't think that would happen to Fly-by-Night.'

'How do they score then?'

'Five for knocking anything down, ten for first refusal, twenty for second, thirty for falling off, ten for not shutting a gate, two for hitting a marker.'

'Oh.' The words went out of Ruth's mind as soon as Peter had spoken them. She could see Pearl, looking very elegant in jade-green tweed, with her long hair blowing in the wind, talking to Mr. McNair; she could see Jane Withenshawe out in the country going at a terrific lick on the bold Clipper; of her parents there was still no sign. The wind was cold and it looked like rain. Ruth felt very sick.

'I'd better go back. There's only three before Woodlark

now,' Peter said.

Ruth followed him back. Mr. McNair came over with the Pymms and Peter had to be polite. Ruth was under no such obligation, which was fortunate, as Pearl said to her, 'Golly, you don't think you're going to get *him* round, do you?'

Ruth glowered at her. She had no wits to think of a reply, so rode off to the other side of the collecting-ring. Peter came past to go to the start, and for one awful moment Ruth could not stop Fly-by-Night from following Wood-lark.

'Not you!' the steward shouted at her, and she managed to turn Fly-by-Night round just in time, before Peter put Woodlark into a canter. She hustled him furiously back into the ring, and saw Pearl grinning.

All the parts of Peter's round that she could see were faultless, and he came back very fast down the hill and flew the jump at the bottom as if it were six times its actual size. When Woodlark came back she was very excited, and Peter had to take her away and walk her about to cool her off, so Ruth did not get a chance to hear how he had done. Mr. McNair was looking very satisfied, and smoking cigars with Mr. Pymm, so Ruth assumed that all was well.

Several of the rounds, from what one could see from the collecting-ring, appeared to be faultless, but what went on in the wood, where all the tricky bits were, was not revealed. The steward, a smart woman in sheepskin and suede, said to her, 'You're the next. Don't go away, will you?' She checked out the next departure, which was Cat's Eyes', and said, 'You're new, aren't you? I haven't seen your pony up here before.'

'Yes—er—no—'

'Don't look so frightened!' the woman said. 'Your pony looks as if he could do it standing on his head.'

Her few kind words wrung a grateful smile out of Ruth.

She watched Cat's Eyes' grey gelding canter very slowly down from the start to stop at the first fence. She realized that she probably would not have to wait much longer, for the grey did not look as if he intended to go any farther. The steward apparently thought so, too, as she said, 'Are you ready, dear?'

Ruth nodded. At the same moment, a yell of 'Ruth!' rent the air, and she turned round, startled, to see Ted and Ron standing at the ropes, looking very out of place in their motor-bike gear and crash-helmets. Ted did a boxer's hand-clasp over his head and shouted, 'Attagirl!'

'Go down to the start now, dear,' said the steward. 'Mercy is eliminated.'

Ruth gave Fly-by-Night a panic-stricken kick with her heels and he bounded forward into a fast trot, nearly cannon-ing into the returning grey, who came home at a far more eager pace than he had left.

'Sorry,' she muttered.

She steered Fly-by-Night for the flag where Major Banks was standing, and managed to pull up in the right place. He checked her number, glanced at his stop-watch, and said, 'Off you go, then.'

Ruth, having somehow expected a roll of drums and a flash of lightning to herald her performance, was amazed to find herself cantering down the hill, completely on her own. The short grass was smooth and inviting, the rails at the bottom looked piffling; beyond, the hill stretched up to the tall elms on its crest where the rooks were cawing and a gleam of sunlight was passing. There wasn't a soul in sight. Ruth no longer felt frightened. She felt excited, and fan-tastically happy.

She knew Fly-by-Night was not going to refuse the rails, by the feel of him. She knew, too, that when she felt like she did now refusals did not happen. She had not waited two years merely to refuse the first fence. Fly-by-Night went over it like Woodlark herself, so big and bold that Ruth almost lost a stirrup, and had to take a clutch of mane to steady herself.

After the jump he steadied himself, and Ruth could feel him wondering what he was up to, galloping across this strange countryside with no Woodlark beside him.

'Come on, Fly. This is in earnest,' Ruth said to him happily, and he flicked an ear back at her, from deep in his thick mane, and Ruth saw the steam of his breath and the shining edge of his eyes, and leaned forward in the saddle, feeling invincible.

The tiger trap into the wood was solid, and Ruth felt the pony's momentary surprise, and instant's doubt. To dispel it, she closed her legs hard. Fly gave a little grunt, and jumped it in a rather unpleasant popping style, which left Ruth up in the air when he was already down. But Peter had said nothing about marks for style. Ruth had a glimpse of a man on a shooting-stick making a mark on his score-sheet, then the roof of the wood closed over her, and Fly-by-Night's hoofs were muffled by the thick, soft ground. She looked up, and saw the marker flag for the left turn just ahead. She pulled up sharply, in a soft smother of leaves, and Fly-by-Night turned on to the narrow detour that led to the fallen log. He was at home in the wood, after all his pounding round the McNair estate; he had learned to do sharp turns through the trees, and scramble under the scrub while Ruth leant close over his withers, ducking for the branches. They came upon the log suddenly. Fly had no time to hesitate; he was over, and Ruth swung him round for the open ride beyond. She had forgotten the tricky jump at the end of the ride, and after the pleasant ease of the canter down the wide path she came to the bank with a lurch of fear. Fly-by-Night went up on the top with more of a scramble than a jump, and then stood there, boggle-eyed, staring into the ditch. Ruth unashamedly took a large bunch of mane in both hands, gave him plenty of rein and drummed hard with her legs.

'Come on! You *must*!'

Her urgency communicated, for after a moment's uneasy pawing at the ground, he jumped out over the ditch and rail in one almighty bound, with such suddenness that only her handfuls of mane kept Ruth aboard. With only a slight pang at her lack of professional poise, she headed Fly-by-Night out across the open grass, and as his shining hoofs flung out beneath her she was full of a sense of exhilaration at what they had already achieved. Even if she did not look smooth and calm like Peter, she got there just the same—so far. At least Ted and Ron and Pearl would see that she had managed half-way; she was not disgraced, whatever happened.

Fly-by-Night seemed to have understood what it was all about now, as if he was enjoying himself, for he flew the first jump out in the open without a moment's hesitation. There was a short stretch across the corner of a field, a jump out over a gap and a bundle of brushwood, then round in a circle, over some straw bales and back towards the wood again. The gate was the next obstacle, and Ruth felt a moment's qualm. She thought perhaps Fly-by-Night wouldn't fancy anything fussy now, after his unimpeded progress over the countryside.

He pulled up in front of the gate because he had to, coming to a halt in long skidding slithers where the ground was already cut up and slippery. Ruth slipped down and took the string off the gate, shoving it open with her foot. Her legs felt all trembly.

'Come on, Fly!'

She was in front of him, pulling him, which he (as if knowing that this procedure was captioned 'Bad' in Ruth's book) did not like. He did not move, but stared at her, his nostrils all wide and red with galloping. Ruth came round to his side and led him properly, and he went through, with a snort of suspicion. Ruth had to heave at him to stop, and managed to get the string back over the post by stretching both arms out to their fullest extent, one holding Fly and one dropping the string. It was not a polished performance, but they had been quite quick.

When she came to mount again she realized immediately that her girths needed tightening, as the saddle started to slither round when she put her weight on the stirrup. She cursed and struggled, with Fly-by-Night going round in circles, heaving up the inch of loose with her clumsy, excited hands. Fly-by-Night trod on her foot, and lunged away into some brambles, and she half hopped, half fell after him, trying to keep him still. The mud was up to her ankles.

'You beast! Wait!'

He waited long enough for her to get half-way back in the saddle, but while she was still in mid-air he set off. Ruth pitched back on the cantle, the reins slithering through her fingers. A branch knocked her cap down over her eyes so that she could not see where she was going: she only knew that there was a great crashing of undergrowth all round her and that twigs and brambles were clawing at her like live animals. Suddenly there was a sharp blow and a pain down the side of her face that made her cry out. A branch seemed to break off with an explosion right in her ear. She thrust her cap back, but could still see nothing but a blur of clutching branches through which Fly-by-Night was forcing his way in a series of excited bounds. Whatever had hit her face was agonizing; she realized that she could not see for blood. When she put her hand up it came away all red.

'Fly, stop it!'

She pulled him to a halt by brute force, tears of sheer rage adding another impediment to her reeling vision. She wiped her face with the back of her sleeve, and peered round for a way out of the predicament Fly had landed her in. There was no sign of a track anywhere, only impenetrable jungle.

'Fly, we're *lost*!' she sobbed. She was outraged—nobody got *lost* in a Hunter Trials! She thought of Pearl, and choked with grief.

'You idiot pony! You beastly idiot pony!'

She mopped frantically at the blood and tears in an effort to see, and kicked Fly on into the thinnest bit of her surroundings that she could find. He crashed through and she bent down, choking and muttering, looking desperately for the salvation of a yellow flag. Suddenly, they were in the open. There were no flags, but at right-angles to their wild stampede through the bush a hoof-churned track appeared. Ruth's sense of direction had become so confused since her blow on the head that she did not know which way to follow the path, but with what she afterwards thought of as a stroke of genius, she thought to look at the hoof-prints. Sunk deep and fast, they showed the way.

Fly-by-Night set off at a canter again, and Ruth tried to sort herself out. She could feel nothing in her face now, and had no idea what had happened, but she did not seem to be feeling in any way indisposed. Rather she felt humiliated and a trifle damp, more with baby tears than blood. 'Oh, you *fool*!' she said to herself, cantering along the path, ashamed and angry. Getting lost, and *crying* . . . she was so incompetent it wasn't true. Reviling herself for her stupidity, she came to the bank without expecting it. Fly-by-Night skidded to a halt and teetered on the lip of it, snorting. Ruth had a glimpse of a startled face staring from the far side, then Fly-by-Night went down in one bound, landing with a great splash in the stream. The person scoring shouted something, but Ruth had no idea what. She was too busy keeping her seat. Fly went through the brush, scattering it with a cracking and a crunching all across the ride, and they were flying away towards the jump out into the open. 'The lovely open!' Ruth thought. She felt as if she had been in the wood for ever, carving her way through, and wondered if she had been given up for lost. All sense of time had left her. She felt she had taken well over the time allowed already. Her eyes stung, and she still could not see very well, but she no longer knew why.

Fly-by-Night, going now as if he would never stop, flew over the fence out into the field. Ruth had to turn him down the hill, but otherwise there was nothing to do, only sit there, and see the people in the collecting-ring on the opposite slope, and think, 'Here I come! I've done it!' She felt wonderful. She did not feel as if she belonged to earth at all. She felt that nothing in the whole world could ever worry her again, nothing could possibly go wrong, nothing could detract. Fly-by-Night went over the ditch at the bottom as if he was Woodlark herself, and then she was back beside Major Banks, who was clicking his stopwatch. 'Steady on!' called the Major.

Ruth heaved, wondering if Fly-by-Night was all set to go round again, but the pony got the message, and dropped into an unseating trot. Ruth bounced and pulled again. Someone came up and took Fly-by-Night's rein and said, 'Whatever have you done to your face?'

'I don't know.' She didn't say it, but she didn't care either. She felt wonderful. She saw Ted and Ron coming towards her, and grinned at them idiotically.

'I say, whatever have you done to your face?' Ted said.

Major Banks came up with the woman out of the collecting-ring and said to her, 'Mrs. Marshall will take you to the First Aid, dear.'

'I think she ought to be put down,' Ted said. 'It's the only humane thing to do.'

Major Banks stared at Ted, and Ted said hastily, 'She's my sister. I'll take her to the First Aid, if you like.'

'Oh, good,' said the Major. 'We can't really spare Mrs. Marshall for a minute or two. It's that van by the Land-Rover. There's a St. John's man there. He'll see to her.'

He looked at Ruth again, rather doubtfully, and went off back to the start. Ruth looked round for Peter, but saw that he was trapped by the Pymms once more, over by the horse-box, so decided she had better get the First Aid chore over. She slid off Fly-by-Night on to her trembly legs, and patted his damp neck.

'Wasn't he marvellous?'

'You did jolly well, from what we could see,' Ron said. 'No more than we expected though. I'll hold Fly if you like, while you go with Ted.'

'Yes, come on, you're losing gore like a stuck pig,' Ted said. 'Come to St. John, where Mercy is eliminated.'

'Where *what*?'

'That's what that woman said. Mercy is eliminated. Didn't you hear her? We liked that, we did.'

Ruth could see that Ted was in one of his dotty moods. They all went to the St. John's Ambulance van, where the man looked very pleased to have something to do. Ruth discovered that her borrowed jacket and tie were all spotted with blood, which worried her more than the wound itself, which, when she was cleaned up, was discovered to be a small but deep cut just below her right eye. It was swelling fast, which was the reason she couldn't see very well.

'You're very lucky, my dear,' said the St. John's man. 'Very lucky it missed your eye.'

Ruth thought it a matter of opinion as to why, as the only injury of the day, she was to be considered lucky, but did not say so. Ted said, 'Very lucky. Mercy is not eliminated after

148

all.'

Ruth was decorated with a sticking-plaster that obscured her vision still further, and given a cup of tea, then she went back up the hill with Ted and Ron, leading Fly-by-Night. The sun, having struggled hard all morning, was just coming out. It had a summer warmth in it, which fitted in: Ruth knew that this was a day when nothing now could go wrong. She was in a stupor of warm, deep-seated bliss. The excitement and the sickening nervousness had given way to a radiance she had never experienced before. She could feel her face smiling idiotically. She could not stop it.

They were almost back at the horse-box when Ted spotted their parents coming across the grass towards them.

'You've missed the act of the century,' Ted greeted them.

'Oh, whatever have you wone to your face?' Mrs. Hollis said to Ruth. 'What happened? Did you fall?'

'No.'

'You got round all right?'

'Yes. A branch hit me, that's all.'

'Oh dear. Never mind. I suppose it was lucky it wasn't your eye. We're terribly sorry we missed you, dear—'

'But you won't be sorry when you hear the reason why,' her father interrupted. Ruth looked at him. He looked quite different from how she had ever seen him before. He looked just like she felt. And she knew the reason why.

'The house?' she said. 'It's all right? She said we could have it—Mr. Lacey's house?'

'That's right. She made up her mind at last. We can move in whenever we like.'

Ruth said nothing. All she could see was the two acres under its covering of snow, the sun shining on it, and the bird marks making lace patterns. She saw Fly-by-Night turned out there, and another, shadowy pony, a companion for Fly. In her dreams, it was Milky Way, in foal to an Arab stallion, never to be hauled about by Pearl again. (Because she knew now that miracles happened.) There was a stable for Fly-by-Night, and a yard paved with bricks . . .

'Say something,' said Ted.

'Please give us your opinion, Miss Hollis.' Ron was grinning.

Her father gave her a little pat on the shoulder and said, 'Leave the child alone. Her constitution isn't up to all this excitement in one day.'

'Her constitution needs a few sandwiches, by the look of it,' her mother said. 'Can't you tie that pony up somewhere, so we can have our lunch?'

Ruth noticed, for the first time, that the event was over and the ponies were all tied up and their owners picnicking. She saw Peter coming up the hill on Woodlark, carrying a red rosette in his hand, and behind him was the bay, Clipper, with a blue rosette tied to his browband. Peter saw her and shouted across:

'Go on! Are you dreaming?'

He came across, grinning. 'Major Banks wants you, over by the Land-Rover.'

'Oh.' Ruth turned to set off for the Land-Rover, but Peter said to her, 'Take Fly, you idiot.'

'What for? Why does he want to see me? My face is all right.'

Peter made a despairing face. He spoke to her very slowly, as if to a foreigner: 'He—wants—to—give—you—a—rosette.'

The miracles were coming in shoals. White as a sheet, Ruth tightened Fly-by-Night's girths and mounted, and followed Peter down to the Land-Rover. (Her parents said to Ted, 'Do you think she's all right? She does look queer.' Ted said, 'She probably thinks she's been killed and has arrived in heaven.' 'Don't talk like that, Ted,' his mother

150

said severely.)

When Major Banks saw Peter he said, 'What, you don't want another one, do you? Wait till ths afternoon.' He was standing with all the score-sheets spread out on a little table, and a boxful of rosettes. He looked very cheerful.

'No, sir, it's Ruth. You said she had won one.'

'Oh, that's right. You came sixth, dear. Very good show. How's your face? All right?'

'Yes, thank you.' Ruth took the white rosette he handed her.

'Lucky it wasn't your eye, eh?'

'Yes, sir.'

'That's the lot, then. Go and have your lunch. Well done.'

Ruth rode slowly back towards the horse-box with Peter. She was speechless. Peter looked at her, smiling.

'Shock too much for you?'

She nodded.

'You'll ride pairs with me this afternoon?' Peter asked.

'Me?'

'Yes, you.'

'Not Clipper? I can't see out of one eye.'

'What does that matter? The other eye's enough, isn't it? Fly'll take you.'

'All right. Yes.'

Ruth rode back to her parents, and Ted and Ron, who were eating sandwiches in the car. When she glanced behind she saw Peter giving his red rosette to Pearl, as if it were a discarded programme. She looked down at her own, shining white in her fingers, and started to count the miracles that had happened that day. The radiance was still spreading. The white rosette would be her dearest treasure until the day of her death.

'Have a sandwich?' said Ted.